D1550176

OTHER BOOKS OF INTEREST

MIDI PROJECTS

by
R. A. PENFOLD

BERNARD BABANI (publishing) LTD
THE GRAMPIANS
SHEPHERDS BUSH ROAD
LONDON W6 7NF
ENGLAND

PLEASE NOTE

Although every care has been taken with the production of this book to ensure that any projects, designs, modifications and/or programs etc. contained herewith, operate in a correct and safe manner and also that any components specified are normally available in Great Britain, the Publishers do not accept responsibility in any way for the failure, including fault in design, of any project, design, modification or program to work correctly or to cause damage to any other equipment that it may be connected to or used in conjunction with, or in respect of any other damage or injury that may be so caused, nor do the Publishers accept responsibility in any way for the failure to obtain specified components.

Notice is also given that if equipment that is still under warranty is modified in any way or used or connected with home-built equipment then that warranty may be void.

First Published — June 1986
Reprinted — January 1990
Reprinted — December 1992

British Library Cataloguing in Publication Data
Penfold, R. A.
  Midi projects.
  1. Music——Data processing   2. Microcomputers
  I. Title
  780'.28'5416   MT723

ISBN 0 85934 156 9

Printed and bound in Great Britain by Cox & Wyman Ltd, Reading

Preface

Although the MIDI interface seems to be regarded by many as the very latest thing in the field of electronic music, at the time of writing this, it has in fact been in existence for a few years. It is only in relatively recent times that it has become popular, and has been adopted by all the main electronic instrument manufacturers. It is not only synthesisers that are fitted with MIDI interfaces these days, but other instruments such as electronic pianos, percussion synthesisers, and even some portable keyboards are now equipped with them. In fact MIDI interfaces are even beginning to appear on some of the more sophisticated effects units such as digital delay lines.

One of the main points of the MIDI interface is that it enables any MIDI equipped instruments, regardless of which manufacturers they originate from, to be easily connected together and used as a sophisticated system. A less well publicised but possibly more important aspect of the MIDI interface is that it permits easy computer control of complex systems, and a few MIDI instruments plus a suitable computer and interface gives the user what is virtually a programmable orchestra. This has obvious attractions to those of limited playing ability, as well as accomplished musicians who require complex accompaniments while playing "live". The main part of this book deals with the missing link, and provides details of interfacing some popular home computers to MIDI systems. The machines covered include the Amstrad CPC 464 and 6128, the Commodore 64 and VIC-20, the BBC model B, the MTX and MSX machines, the Sinclair QL, Spectrum, and ZX81, and others. Other subjects covered include interfacing MIDI equipment to analogue synthesisers, and interfacing MIDI systems to percussion synthesisers.

R. A. Penfold

CONTENTS

Chapter 1

MIDI BASICS

Despite the major changes and advances in the world of electronic music over the past few years, the widespread acceptance of the MIDI standard by the major instrument manufacturers would still have to be considered as probably the most significant development so far. The basic idea of MIDI is a simple, perhaps obvious one, and it is intended to enable one electronic instrument to be used to control another instrument so that the two can effectively be combined to operate as a single instrument. In fact it is quite feasable to have several instruments MIDI linked, and effectively operating as one large and sophisticated instrument.

Linking of electronic instruments has been possible in the past, but usually only in a fairly basic manner. Also, if you had instruments from a variety of manufacturers there could be difficulties in getting one instrument to control another. In some cases a special lead or a simple interface would be all that were required, but in other cases it would be impossible to provide effective links between the instruments. MIDI, which stands for "Musical Instrument Digital Interface", is intended to enable any MIDI equipped instrument (or other device) to be connected to and used with any other item of MIDI equipment, regardless of just what the particular instruments happen to be, and which manufacturer(s) produced them. Furthermore, it is not just a very basic system which gives gating information, or note values. It is designed to be able to communicate other information such as how hard a key is depressed on a touch sensitive keyboard. On the other hand, an instrument which only requires something fairly basic like gate pulses can still be used with a more sophisticated instrument, and it will be designed to simply ignore any information which is superfluous to its operation. It is therefore quite possible to use (say) a touch sensitive sixteen channel synthesiser with an electronic drum kit, provided both have a MIDI interface of course.

Computer Control

Although we have so far only considered the possibility of connecting one MIDI instrument to another, what makes the

1

MIDI interface particularly useful is the possibility of computer control. Interfacing a home computer to a MIDI instrument is not very difficult in most cases, and it can greatly increase the versatility of the instrument. In particular, there is the possibility of using (say) a polyphonic synthesiser plus a percussion synthesiser with a composer style program. Many home computers have built-in sound generators which can generate quite impressive music when used with a good composer program, but they do not compare with the results that can be obtained with synthesisers, electric pianos, and other MIDI equipped instruments that are now available. With a home computer, suitable software, and one or two MIDI equipped instruments, you have what is virtually a personal orchestra. Coupled with the falling cost of electronic instruments, it is this factor that makes MIDI such a significant development. It is now possible to put together in ones own home and at reasonable cost a set up that would have not so long ago filled a professional studio to the brim, and which would have cost about as much as the average family house.

Serial Data
Before considering some practical MIDI projects it would perhaps be as well to explain some basics of MIDI operation. It is quite possible to fit together some MIDI equipment and to use it successfully without having any real understanding of how the system functions. However, armed with a reasonable knowledge of the subject it is much easier to sort out any problems which might crop up, and it opens up the possibility of using the system in a way that precisely matches your needs, rather than perhaps having to settle for a ready made set up that does not quite meet your exact requirements. This is particularly so with a computer controlled set up where it introduces the possibility of writing software to provide exactly the functions you require.

An important difference between the MIDI system and the gate/CV (control voltage) system which it has replaced, is that it is fully digital. All the MIDI system does is to pass integer values in the range 0 to 255 from one instrument to another. It is up to each instrument or other MIDI device to transmit the correct series of values, and to correctly interpret and act upon any values that are received.

MIDI is a form of serial interface, and it has strong similarities to the RS232C and RS423 serial interfaces used in computing. The values are sent in binary form, and for those who are not familiar with this numbering system it should perhaps be explained that it only uses the numbers 0 and 1. This is convenient for an electronic system in that the number 1 can be represented by a "high" voltage which in practice is usually about 5 volts, and a 0 can be represented by a "low" voltage (usually little more than 0 volts). Circuits having ten output voltage levels to represent numbers from 0 to 9 would be feasable, but would be difficult to use and rather complex in practice.

The table given below should help to explain the way in which the binary system operates. It simply shows the decimal number that each digit of an 8 bit binary number represents when it is set to 1. A digit does, of course, always represent 0 when it is set to 0.

Bit 7	Bit 6	Bit 5	Bit 4	Bit 3	Bit 2	Bit 1	Bit 0
128	64	32	16	8	4	2	1

As a simple example, the binary number 10001001 is equivalent to 137 in the ordinary decimal numbering system (128+8+1=137). The maximum number that can be handled by 8 bits (binary digits) is obviously 11111111 in binary, which is equivalent to 255 in decimal. It is this that restricts the 8 bit MIDI system to the 0 to 255 range of values referred to earlier.

Digital circuits normally move data around internally in parallel form. In other words, each device has eight inputs and (or) eight outputs so that data can be transferred 8 bits at a time. This system is sometimes used when sending data from one piece of equipment to another, but it has its drawbacks. One of these is the the need for multiway cables to connect the various items together, and these cables tend to be quite expensive. A more major problem is that of stray coupling causing signals on one lead in the cable to be coupled into other leads. To avoid this it is often necessary to restrict the cable length to no more than a couple of metres. The alternative to parallel connection is some kind of serial interface, such as the one used in the MIDI system. In a serial system the data is transmitted on just one line (plus an earth line), but this obviously precludes simultaneous transmission of all the bits. Instead they must be transmitted one at a time, and with most serial systems (including the MIDI one) the least significant bit is sent first, running through in sequence to the most significant bit. This has the advantage of only needing two wires to connect one item of equipment to another, rather than about nine to a couple of dozen wires (depending on the exact form of the parallel interface concerned). With serial data systems it is not normally necessary to have screening leads, or to keep connecting leads particularly short. With serial data systems quite long leads can usually be accommodated without any problems, and although the MIDI type is quite fast it can still operate at up to at least 15 metres using just two connecting wires.

In the fundamental form outlined above a serial system can not operate properly, since the receiving equipment will have no way of knowing when to test the transmission line to determine the state of each bit. One way around the problem is to use a synchronous system where a third line is used to carry a clock signal or some other form of synchronisation signal to indicate the start of each data stream. Most serial systems are asynchronous though, and the MIDI system falls into this catagory. With this system there are no additional connection lines, but instead additional bits are transmitted along with the data bits. Of most importance is the "start" bit, and this indicates to the receiving equipment that it must sample the data line at regular intervals thereafter until the state of each bit has been detected. With most practical systems one or two extra bits are added onto the end of each byte, and these are called "stop" bits. These are just used as part of a simple form of error checking and to ensure that the blocks of 8 bits (bytes) are spaced out and do not merge into one another. Extra bits called "parity" bits are sometimes added, and these are again used as part of a simple error checking process. However, these do not apply to MIDI interfaces. Figure 1 illustrates the way in which serial data is transmitted, and this might help to clarify the system for you.

There are a number of different word formats in common use in serial systems, but for MIDI purposes 1 start bit, 8 data bits, 1 stop bit, and no parity is the only one that is used. Serial data systems use a variety of baud rates, and there are several standard ones from 50 to 19200 baud. The baud rate is simply the number of bits transmitted per second if there is a continuous data stream. The MIDI system originally operated at 19200 baud, but it was criticised for being too slow (despite the fact that this is the fastest rate in common use apart from the final MIDI system). In fact a baud rate of 19200 is not quite as fast as it might at first appear, bearing in mind that ten bits must be transmitted to transfer one byte of information. This gives an absolute maximum of 1920

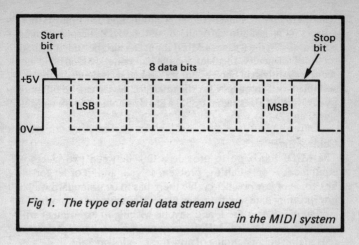

Fig 1. The type of serial data stream used
in the MIDI system

bytes per second, or just over 0.5ms per byte. Even taking into account that three bytes normally need to be transmitted to produce each action from the instrument, and that several channels may be controlled, it would still take just a few milliseconds to send blocks of data. Whether or not this would produce audible problems is debatable, but in the final system the baud rate was increased to 31250 baud.

The MIDI system is essentially the same as the RS232C and RS423 serial ports fitted to many home computers, but in points of detail there are problems which make it highly unlikely that a serial output from a computer could be used to drive a MIDI input. The first problem is that MIDI interfaces use standard 5 volt TTL levels, and normally have opto-isolator inputs to avoid problems with earth loops. RS232C ports use signal levels of nominally plus and minus 12 volts (plus and minus 5 volts in the case of the RS423) with no form of isolation at the inputs. This incompatibility could be overcome with suitable signal processing stages, but there is a more difficult problem with the baud rate. 31250 baud is not a standard rate, and it is not one that can be achieved with any home computer I have encountered. It might be possible to modify the serial interface to operate at the correct baud rate, but this would almost certainly render it unusable for other purposes, and would probably not be a very good idea.

As we shall see later, the integrated circuits that are intended primarily for use in RS232C and similar interfaces can be made to work perfectly well in a MIDI application, and using one of these devices it is not too difficult to add a MIDI output to most computers. In most cases a MIDI input can also be added without too much difficulty. Incidentally, the baud rate of 31250 baud may seem a slightly odd choice, but it is in fact a convenient one as a suitable clock frequency for the interface device can be obtained by dividing a 1MHz signal by 32, a 2MHz signal by 64, or a 4MHz signal by 128.

Control Bytes
The MIDI hardware to provide a link between two pieces of equipment is only half the problem solved, and in order for the link to be of any practical value there has to be a standard way of interpretting data sent from one piece of equipment to another. A system of codes is used, and anyone wishing to experiment with computer control of MIDI equipment must have at least a reasonable understanding of how these codes operate.

Three bytes are needed to send each note to the synthesiser, and these provide the following functions:-

Byte 1   Status information which indicates that the following two bytes refer to the triggering of a note, and the MIDI channel number.
Byte 2   The note value
Byte 3   The velocity value.

There are sixteen MIDI channels available, and these are selected using numbers from 0 to 15. This can cause confusion since you will often find references to MIDI channels being in the range 1 to 16. The difference is that the 1 to 16 range is merely used for identification purposes, whereas numbers from 0 to 15 are actually used to select these channels. Thus, if you have a synthesiser which operates on channel 12, the channel value used to direct data to it would be 11. Some instruments will only operate on one particular channel, but with most modern instruments you can set up the instrument to operate on any desired channel.

Of course, the point of having several channels is to enable several instuments to be fed from a MIDI output, with each instrument only responding to the particular data which is intended for it (and contains the right channel identification number). It is possible to have two instruments using the same channel, but only if they must both be fed with the same data. If you have a polyphonic synthesiser or other multichannel instrument it will almost certainly have the option of a separate MIDI channel for each voice, so that each voice can be independently controlled. Incidentally, most MIDI instruments have three MIDI sockets. These are separate input and output sockets, plus a MIDI THRU socket. The latter simply enables the data fed to the input socket to be easily tapped off and connected through to another instrument. In this way several instruments can be controlled from a single MIDI output if desired. Figure 2 shows a typical set up for a MIDI controller and several instruments.

The velocity value only applies to touch sensitive instruments, but this byte will still be transmitted by instruments that lack this facility. They will usually transmit the maximum value of 127. It is essential that this byte is transmitted in order to maintain

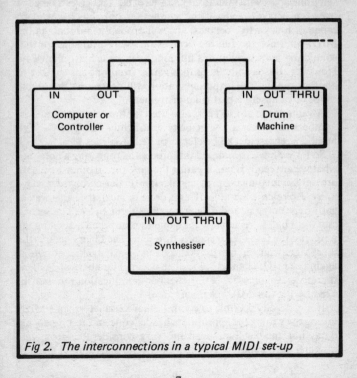

Fig 2. The interconnections in a typical MIDI set-up

compatibility between MIDI instruments of various types. If some instruments were to transmit more bytes per note than others this would obviously prevent them from operating properly together. Of course, a non-touch sensitive instrument will simply discard the value in the velocity byte and can not make use of it.

If we now examine each byte in a little more detail, the header byte is divided into two 4 bit nibbles. The most significant nibble is set to 1001 to indicate that a note is to be triggered. The least significant nibble contains the channel number. Thus 10010011 would specify that a note is to be triggered (1001) on channel 4 (0011). Few computers permit numbers to be entered in binary form, and this is a rather long winded way of doing things anyway. Rationalising things, the first byte is equal to 143 plus the MIDI channel identification number (or 144 plus the true MIDI channel value).

The note value is in the range 1 to 127, and the notes are spaced a semitone apart with middle C at a value of 60. This gives a range of over ten octaves. Even if the synthesiser only has a keyboard range of four or five octaves, you will probably find that via the MIDI interface the full ten octaves or so are available, or that something approaching this full range can be achieved anyway. However, this is something that varies from one instrument to another, and a little experimentation will determine the usable range of values for a particular instrument.

A value range of 1 to 127 is also used for the velocity byte. Low numbers represent a low velocity or a lightly struck key – high numbers represent a high velocity or heavily struck key.

So far we have considered this process as triggering a note, but what we are really doing is gating the note on. In other words we are only simulating the pressing of a key on the keyboard, and we must also release the note. This is done in much the same way as gating the note on, and it again requires three bytes. The second and third bytes are actually the same as used when activating the note, but the first byte is slightly different. The binary code in the most significant nibble is 1000, but the least significant byte is again the MIDI channel value. The decimal number used here is therefore 127 plus the MIDI channel identification number, or 128 plus the true MIDI channel value.

It is generally possible to control other parameters via a MIDI interface by using the appropriate header code and accompanying data, but the facilities available vary considerably from one instrument to another. The instrument's manual should give full details of what can be controlled via the MIDI interface, together with the appropriate control code details. It is not essential to use codes other than those outlined above, since they provide control of the important parameters, and enable multichannel touch sensitive sequencing to be achieved. Each voice can be adjusted to give the desired effect prior to starting a sequence, and it is not necessary to undertake this type of thing via the MIDI interface unless changes are required during a sequence. One feature that is certainly very useful (where it is available) is pitch bend. Many synthesisers permit the pitch to be varied in such small increments that there is no noticeable jumping in pitch, and the effect is indistinguishable from pitch bend on an analogue instrument. Some parameters can only be controlled via the MIDI interface if they are enabled from the front panel controls using the appropriate set of settings. The manuals for your instruments should give details of how to enable MIDI control of any functions of this type, together with details of the header codes used for each one, etc.

Modes

There are three common MIDI operating modes, and these were originally called "Omni", "Poly", and "Mono", but these names have now been replaced with numbers 1, 3, and 4 respectively. The most sophisticated instruments have all three modes, but the more simple types just have one or two modes. The basic idea is to choose a mode that, where necessary, effectively brings the sophisticated instrument controlling the system down to the same level as the less sophisticated one that is being controlled.

Omni (1)

All instruments default to this mode at switch-on, and all MIDI instruments therefore have this mode. In this mode the receiving equipment will respond to note on/off information regardless of what channel it is on. Just how individual voices of a polyphonic instrument respond to received notes depends on the method of internal assignment used on the instrument concerned. The main point of this mode is that it enables a number of instruments to be controlled from one instrument (or controller), and all the instruments will play in unison.

Poly (3)

In this mode instruments can be assigned to a certain channel, and data can therefore be directed to just one instrument even if several instruments are being fed from a single source. As for the omni mode, just how an instrument responds to each note depends on its method of internal assignment.

Mono (4)

If an instrument has several channels, each with a different voice, by using this mode it is possible to assign each voice to a separate MIDI channel, but they must be consecutive channels. If you are using a computer to provide multipart sequencing then this is the best mode to choose, as it gives individual control over each voice. For monophonic sequencing the default (omni) mode will suffice.

There is a mode 2 incidentally, but (at the time of writing this anyway) it is exclusive to Yamaha synthesisers. It simply gets all channels of all synthesisers to play the same notes.

This covers the main principles of MIDI interfacing, and if you understand the points covered in this chapter you should be able to use MIDI equipment, including the home constructed projects described in subsequent chapters, with little difficulty. One additional point worth making though, is that it is well worthwhile studying the manuals for the MIDI equipped instruments in your music system. These should give useful information on just what can and can not be achieved via the MIDI interface with your particular instruments.

Chapter 2

COMPUTER INTERFACING

While the ability to control one instrument from another via their MIDI intefaces is undoubtedly a very useful feature, greater possibilities are made available by using computer control. In particular, a suitable home computer plus the appropriate software can act as a sophisticated step-time sequencer having a note capacity of several thousand notes. Real-time sequencing is also possible, although as we shall see later this is a little more difficult to achieve. Also, more and more instruments coming onto the market have some form of built-in real-time sequencer, but built-in step-time sequencers are still relatively rare.

In this chapter we will consider some MIDI interfaces for a variety of popular computers. Virtually any computer could be used as the basis of a MIDI controller, but ideally a machine with good input/output capability and a fairly large memory capacity should be used. This does not necessarily mean basing the system on an expensive machine, and a computer such as the Sinclair Spectrum (any version) is perfectly suitable for this application.

6402 UART
A MIDI interface can be provided by virtually any of the serial interface devices that are normally used for RS232C serial ports, such as the 6850 or Z80 DART. The high baud rate is not a real problem as most serial interface devices will operate at maximum baud rates of around 250 to 500 kilobaud. Most serial interface devices are designed to connect direct to the buses of one particular microprocessor family, but there is one type which is intended for general purpose use, and this is the UART (universal asynchronous transmitter/receiver). Apart from being readily usable with practically any microprocessor, a UART can also be used in stand-alone units (a feature which is exploited in some of the circuits featured in the next chapter).

The UART utilized in many of the circuits in this book is the industry standard type, the 6402. Before going on to consider some circuits based on this device we will consider its method of operation. Figure 3 shows pinout details for this device.

Serial transmission is very straightforward, with the eight (parallel) bits of data from the computer or other source being fed

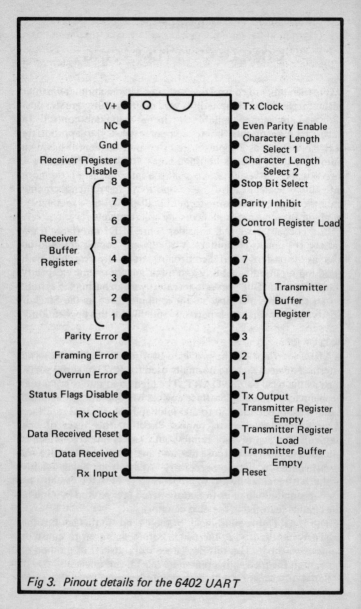

Fig 3. Pinout details for the 6402 UART

12

to the eight lines of the transmitter buffer register. This does not in itself result in the data being transmitted, and to achieve this the Transmitter Register Load input must be pulsed low. The data is then latched into the transmitter buffer register, transferred into the transmitter register, and then clocked out of here in serial form on the TX Output terminal. This double buffering is common with serial devices, and it enables fresh data to be received before the previous byte has been fully transmitted. Two status outputs (pins 22 and 24) indicate whether or not their respective buffers are empty, and these can be read by a digital input of the computer or other device and used to hold-off fresh data until the device is ready to receive it.

The transmitter baud rate is controlled by the clock signal applied to the TX clock input, and the baud rate is one sixteenth of the clock frequency. The word format is controlled by five programming pins (35 to 39), and these enable any standard word format to be obtained by connecting each terminal to the appropriate supply rail. The Control Register Load input can be pulsed high to load the logic states on the five programming terminals into the device, or this input can simply be tied continuously to the positive supply rail.

Received data is fed to the RX Input, and is clocked into the received data register. It is then transferred to the receiver buffer register, and is then available on the eight bit parallel output. There is a separate receiver clock input, and the clock frequency is again sixteen times the baud rate. There are three status outputs which indicate various types of receiving error, but these are not of much use in the present context, where any corruption of data will usually be devastatingly obvious.

All the outputs of the device are three-state types. In other words, they can be set to the disabled mode where they have a high output impedance and will assume whatever state any logic output driving them should dictate. This is essential for direct interfacing to the busses of a computer, where the outputs must normally be in the disabled state, and should only switch to the active state when they are read by the microprocessor. An important status output of the receiver section is the Data Received output at pin 19. This goes high when a fresh byte is received. In use this output is monitored by the program which prevents the received data register from being read until the Data Received output goes high. This avoids having each byte of data read several times. Reading the received data register does not automatically clear the Data Received flag, and this must be done by supplying a low pulse to the Data Received Reset input at pin 18.

Apart from the supply pins and pin 2 (which is unused), the only terminal not discussed so far is the reset input. This is merely supplied with a positive pulse at switch-on.

MIDI Output

Figure 4 shows the circuit diagram of a simple MIDI interface that can be connected to the user port (or some similar facility) of several popular home computers. Where this method is applicable it will almost certainly represent the easiest way of adding a MIDI interface to a computer. Figure 4 includes connection details for use with the BBC model B and VIC-20 user ports. PB0 to PB7 are used to drive the eight data inputs of UART IC1, and CB2 drives the TBRL (transmitter buffer register load) input. As explained previously, the latter must be pulsed low in order to load the eight bits of data into the transmitter buffer register, from where they are then loaded into the transmitter register and transmitted in serial form. With the suggested method of connection CB2 would be used in the mode where it automatically provides a negative output pulse after each write operation to the user port. This is very convenient as it results in any data written to the user port being automatically transmitted from the serial output of IC1. If the interface is used with the Commodore 64 it would be possible to obtain similar results by using PC2 instead of CB2. With other computers it might be necessary to use an ordinary digital output with sofware generating the negative pulse on TBRL. Another possibility worth investigating would be to drive the circuit from a parallel printer output, with the Strobe line being used to drive TBRL. However, this would only work with a printer port that can provide full 8 bit output codes (some, including the Amstrad machines, can only give seven bits of data, with the most significant bit always being low).

C1 and R1 provide a long reset pulse to IC1 at switch-on. IC2a is a 2 input NOR gate but it is used here as an inverter at the serial output of IC1. This is essential as the direct serial output from IC1 is of the wrong polarity, and it would have no effect if coupled to a MIDI input. With IC1 having a built-in divide by 16 action at the clock input it consequently requires a clock frequency at 16 x 31250, or 500kHz in other words. The clock signal is provided by

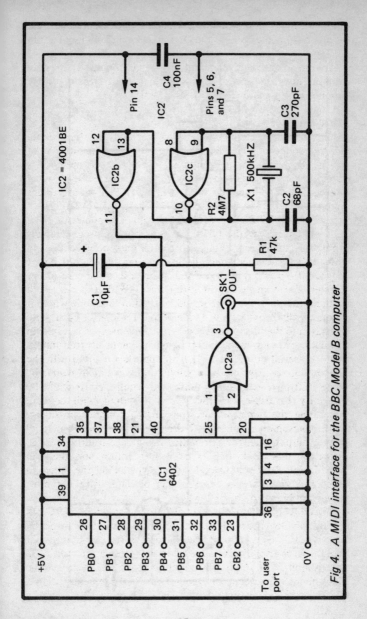

Fig 4. A MIDI interface for the BBC Model B computer

15

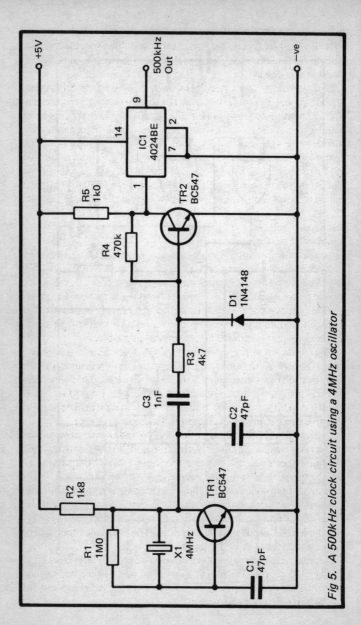

Fig 5. A 500kHz clock circuit using a 4MHz oscillator

16

two gates of IC2 which are used in a simple crystal oscillator circuit. A 500kHz ceramic resonator is suitable as an inexpensive substitute for crystal X1 incidentally. The fourth gate of IC2 is not used in this circuit.

An alternative clock circuit is shown in Figure 5, and this uses a 4MHz crystal oscillator based on Tr1 to drive a squaring amplifier (Tr2) and a three stage binary divider circuit. The latter is three stages of a CMOS 4024BE seven stage ripple counter, and it divides the 4MHz signal by eight to give the required 500kHz output frequency. This circuit is obviously a little more complex and expensive than using a 500kHz crystal or resonator, but it has the advantage of using a crystal that is widely available at quite modest cost. Another alternative is shown in the circuit of Figure 6, and this is similar to the circuit of Figure 5. However, the oscillator operates at 1MHz and IC1 is a D type flip/flop connected to operate as a divide by two circuit. IC1 is actually a dual D type flip/flop, but in this circuit one section of the device is left unused. A 1MHz crystal is probably the most readily available type, although they can be relatively expensive. It would be possible to use a 2MHz oscillator feeding a two stage binary divider, but as 2MHz crystals are both relatively expensive and difficult to obtain this would probably only be worthwhile if you happen to have a suitable crystal in the spares box.

As explained in the description of the UART, it can handle a wide range of different word formats by programming the appropriate five inputs (pins 35 to 39). The method of connection shown in Figure 4 gives the correct mode with 1 start bit, 8 data bits, 1 stop bit, and no parity bit. Pin 34 is tied high in order to load the five programming levels into IC1's control register.

Although the 6402 is capable of both serial transmission and reception, in this circuit only the transmitter section is utilized. The interface consequently only provides a MIDI output and no MIDI input. For step-time sequencing an output is all that is required, but obviously real-time sequencing is not possible with this very basic interface circuit. Real-time sequencing requires note values and other information to be read from the keyboard via the MIDI output of the instrument. This is a topic which will be dealt with later in this chapter.

The standard type of plug/socket used for MIDI interfaces is the 5 way (180 degree) DIN type. Figure 7 shows the correct method of connecting the output of the interface to the MIDI input of the synthesiser or other instrument.

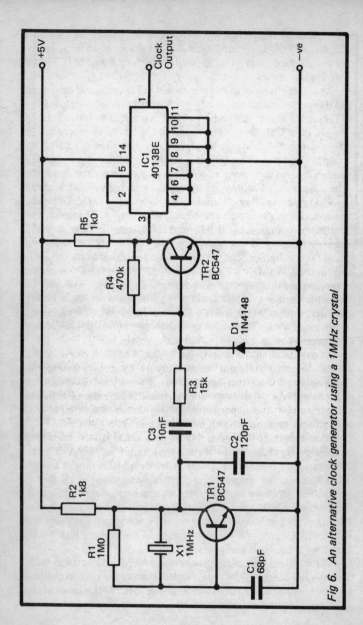

Fig 6. An alternative clock generator using a 1MHz crystal

18

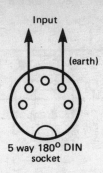

Input

(earth)

5 way 180° DIN
socket

Fig 7. The connections to the MIDI input socket

If the interface is used with a BBC model B computer it is connected to the user port via a 20 way IDC header socket fitted with about half to one metre of cable. The Commodore VIC-20 and 64 computers both require a 2 by 12 way 0.156 inch edge connector to make the connections to their user ports. Suitable connectors are readily available, but not fitted with the appropriate polarising key. Great care therefore has to be taken in order to avoid fitting the connector up side down (which could result in the inteface being damaged). With a little ingenuity it might be possible to add a polarising key, but I prefer the simple alternative of clearly labelling the top and bottom edges of the connector as such. Connection details for all three computers are shown in Figure 8. Note that line PC2 of the user port must be used in place of line CB2 in the case of the Commodore 64 machine.

Basic MIDI Interface Components (Fig. 4)
Resistors all ¼ watt 5%
R1   47k
R2   4M7

Capacitors
C1   10µF 25V electrolytic
C2   68pF ceramic
C3   270pF ceramic

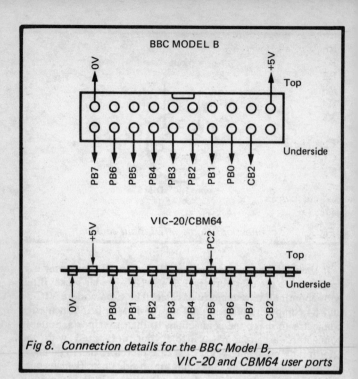

Fig 8. Connection details for the BBC Model B,
VIC-20 and CBM64 user ports

C4	100nF ceramic

Semiconductors
IC1	6402
IC2	4001BE

Miscellaneous
SK1	5 way DIN socket
X1	500kHz crystal or ceramic resonator

40 pin DIL IC holder
14 pin DIL IC holder
Computer connector and cable
5 way DIN cable
Circuit board, case, etc.

Clock Generator (4MHz) Components (Fig. 5)
Resistors all ¼ watt 5%

R1	1M
R2	1k8
R3	4k7
R4	470k
R5	1k

Capacitors

C1, C2	47pF ceramic
C3	1nF polyester

Semiconductors

Tr1, Tr2	BC547
IC1	4024BE
D1	1N4148

Miscellaneous

X1	4MHz wire-ended crystal

14 pin DIL IC holder, circuit board, etc.

Clock Generator (1MHz) Components (Fig. 6)
Resistors all ¼ watt 5%

R1	1M
R2	1k8
R3	15k
R4	470k
R5	1k

Capacitors

C1	68pF ceramic
C2	120pF ceramic
C3	10nF polyester

Semiconductors

Tr1, Tr2	BC547
IC1	4013BE
D1	1N4148

Miscellaneous

X1	1MHz crystal and holder

14 pin DIL IC holder, circuit board, etc.

Software

This simple program for the BBC model B computer shows the basic way in which notes are written to the instrument.

```
5 REM BBC MIDI PROG
10 ?&FE6C=160
20 ?&FE62=255
30 READ A,B
40 IF A=0 THEN END
50 ?&FE60=150:?&FE60=A:?&FE60=127
60 FOR D=1 TO B:NEXT
70 ?&FE60=134:?&FE60=A:?&FE60=0
80 GOTO 30
90 DATA 60,500,62,500,64,500,65,500,67,500,69,500,
71,500,72,1000,0,0
```

Line 10 sets CB2 for the correct operating mode, and line 20 sets PB0 to PB7 as outputs. Note (A) and duration (B) values are READ at line 30 from the DATA statement at line 90. The sample values give a rising scale of C major starting at middle C, but these could obviously be replaced with any desired values. The final two values must be 0, and this ends the sequence properly at line 40 rather than just letting the program crash to a halt. The notes are gated on at line 50, and we are using channel 7 here, but any other channel could be used if necessary. For monophonic sequencing the omni mode is suitable and the channel number is then irrelevant. The FOR..NEXT loop at line 60 sets the duration of each note before it is gated off at line 70. The program is looped by line 80 until the sequence is halted.

This simple program should give you the general idea of the way in which sequencing can be accomplished via a MIDI interface. For multichannel sequencing it would be preferable to use machine code so as to obtain better synchronisation between channels, although most versions of BASIC will give good results with two, three, and in some cases four channel operation. When using BASIC there is no danger of one byte being fed to the interface before the previous one has been processed, but the higher speed of machine code does open up this possibility. One way around the problem would be to monitor the TBRE (transmitter buffer register empty) output at pin 22 of IC1. This goes high when the buffer is empty and the device is ready for the next byte of data. Together with suitable software this could provide a suitable hold-action. However, in practice it would probably be easier to use a timing loop to space out bytes of data by around $350\mu s$.

This simple program is the VIC-20 equivalent of the BBC model B MIDI program discussed above.

```
5 REM VIC-20 MIDI PROG
10 POKE 37138,255
20 POKE 37148,160
30 READ A,B
40 IF A=0 THEN END
50 POKE 37136,150:POKE 37136,A:POKE 37136,127
60 FOR D=1 TO B:NEXT
70 POKE 37136,134:POKE 37136,A:POKE 37136,0
80 GOTO 30
90 DATA 60,250,62,250,64,250,65,250,67,250,69,250,
   71,250,72,500,0,0
```

This program is essentially the same as the original, but obviously the port addresses have been changed to suit the VIC-20 computer. Also, the VIC-20's BASIC uses the standard POKE instruction rather than the usual system used in the BBC model B computer.

Finally, the program given below is the version for the Commodore 64.

```
5 REM CBM64 MIDI PROG
10 POKE 56579,255
20 READ A,B
30 IF A=0 THEN END
40 POKE 56577,150:POKE 56577,A:POKE 56577,127
50 FOR D=1 TO B:NEXT
60 POKE 56577,134:POKE 56577,A:POKE 56577,0
70 GOTO 20
80 DATA 60,250,62,250,64,250,65,250,67,250,69,250,
   71,250,72,500,0,0
```

Again this is essentially the same program, but with the port addresses changed. Also, in this case there is no need to set up

23

PC2 for the correct operating mode, as unlike CB2 of the other two computers, it has just one mode of operation.

There is insufficient space available in this book to permit a complex sequencer program to be included for every home computer, but it is not too difficult to add features to the basic routines. For instance, things such as the ability to vary the tempo and to edit note sequences. Graphics can also be used, although this inevitably complicates the program quite considerably. This brings a couple of attendant disadvantages, one of which is simply that grahpics displays generally take up a lot of memory, leaving less for note storage. The other is that unless due care is taken, the graphics might slow down or in some other way affect the timing of the program.

Bus Interfacing

If you do not have a computer with a suitable user port, or you require a MIDI input as well as a MIDI output, this can be achieved by interfacing a serial device direct to the computer's busses. It is only fair to point out though, that this is probably not something that should be tackled by complete beginners to electronics construction. A mistake could potentially cause a lot of expensive damage to the computer. Although the risk is not a major one, and modern digital integrated circuits are quite robust, it is one that is probably best avoided.

Most computers provide access to the busses of the machine plus some other useful lines, but the exact description of the port concerned varies from one manufacturer to another. It is usually called either the "expansion" port or the "cartridge" port though. We will start with an interface based on a UART which can be used with the cartridge port of the VIC-20 or Commodore 64 machines, or with slight modification it can be made to operate with the BBC model B computer. In the case of the latter it connects to the "1MHz Bus".

The basic circuit diagram of the interface appears in Figure 9. The circuit is complete except that it requires a clock generator of some kind. For use with the VIC-20 computer one of the clock circuits for the MIDI interface described earlier (Figure 4) must be used. With the BBC and Commodore 64 machines there is an easier solution, and this will be dealt with shortly.

Starting with the MIDI side of the circuit, Tr1 inverts the serial output from UART IC1 and provides a high enough current to drive a MIDI input reliably. IC3 is the opto-isolator at the MIDI

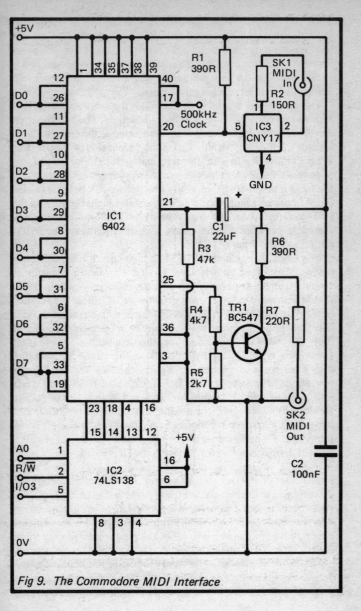

Fig 9. The Commodore MIDI Interface

25

input. For those who are unfamiliar with devices of this type it should perhaps be explained that an opto-isolator consists of a light emitting diode with its light output directed towards some form of semiconductor light sensor. The two components are encapsulated in an opaque casing which is needed to prevent ambient light from reaching the sensor.

The opto-isolator used in this circuit is the most common type, with an npn photo-transistor as the light sensor. The MIDI output drives the input LED, while R1 is connected as the collector load resistor for the photo-transistor on the output side of the isolator. In effect the collector – emitter terminals of the device act as a sort of photo–resistor, and they provide a very high resistance when the LED is switched off, or a very low resistance when it is turned on. R1 normally pulls the serial input of IC1 high, but driving the LED on results in the input being taken low. The isolator therefore provides the necessary inversion between the MIDI output and the input of IC1.

The CNY17 specified for IC3 is a high speed, high efficiency device. Any other opto-isolator having a minimum transfer of 100%, high speed operation, and the standard 6 pin encapsulation should also work in the circuit perfectly well. Ordinary types such as the popular TIL111 might work in the circuit, but some devices may provide an inadequate signal transfer or operating speed, and they are not recommended for this application. Note that Darlington types are totally unusable in this circuit, as although they have good signal transfer figures they are far too slow in operation. Note also, that the base terminal of IC3 (pin 6) is left unconnected (pin 3 of the device is not connected internally incidentally). Of course, the point of using an opto-isolator is that it avoids any direct connection between the items of equipment in the system. One advantage this brings is the avoidance of any hum or earth loops. Another advantage is that it prevents any damage if there is a large voltage difference between the chassis connections of any items in the system. There is no danger of this if everything in the system is earthed to the mains earth, but it can easily occur if one or more items in the system have dual insulation with the mains earth lead being left unused. Many pieces of mains operated equipment seem to be of the dual insulated type these days.

The eight bit parallel inputs and outputs of IC1 connect to the data bus of the computer. Additionally, the Data Received status output connects to D7 of the data bus. Data is continuously being placed onto and read from the data bus, and the control inputs of IC1 must be fed with signals that cause it to receive any data written to it but no other data, or to place requested data onto the data bus at the correct times. This is achieved by decoding the address and control buses, but in the VIC-20 most of the decoding is done internally.

In this case we are using line I/O3, which pulses low when any address in the range 39936 to 40959 is accessed. This line is fed one of IC2's negative enable inputs, and IC2 is therefore enabled when any address in the specified range is accessed (the other negative enable input and the positive enable input are simply tied to 0V and +5V respectively). IC2 is a 3 to 8 line decoder, but here one of the inputs is connected to earth, and it effectively becomes a 2 to 4 line decoder. With I/O3 activated one of the four lines goes to the low state, and which of the lines it is depends on the states of A0 and R/W. One output line is used to operate the Transmitter Buffer Register Load input of IC1 when data on the data bus is to be transmitted, and another activates the enable input of the received data buffer register when the computer is reading a received value. The third line resets the Data Received flag (via the Data Received Reset input), and the fourth line drives the Status Flags Enable input. The latter permits the Data Received flag to be monitored by the computer via D7 of the data bus.

Rationalising things, the interface occupies two addresses, both of which are used for read and write operations, as detailed below:-

Read 39936	Read received values
Write 39936	Transmit values
Read 39937	Read Data Received status flag
Write 39937	Reset Data received status flag

In fact the interface appears as echoes throughout the 39936 to 40959 address range, but the base addresses are as good as any others in the range.

Commodore MIDI Interface Components (Fig. 9)
Resistors all ¼ watt 5%
R1	390R
R2	150R
R3	47k
R4	4k7

27

R5	2k7
R6	390R
R7	220R

Capacitors

| C1 | 22μF electolytic |
| C2 | 100nF ceramic |

Semiconductors

IC1	6402
IC2	74LS138
IC3	CNY17
Tr1	BC547

Miscellaneous

| SK1, SK2 | 5 way (180 degree) DIN socket |

Computer connector and lead, 40 pin DIL IC holder, 16 pin DIL IC holder, case, circuit board, etc.

Additionally a clock generator circuit is required. The text and diagrams give details of modifications for machines other than the Commodore 64 and VIC-20.

Making Connections

One difficulty with interfacing to the VIC-20's cartridge port is that it requires a 2 by 22 way 0.156 inch pitch male edge connector. Ready made connectors of this type do not seem to be available. In fact male edge connectors are just pieces of printed circuit board with the appropriate number of tracks at the correct spacing. In this case 22 tracks spaced 0.156 inches apart are needed, on each side of the board. It is quite easy to make up a connector using an etch resist pen or rub-down etch resistant transfers, but care has to be taken in order to ensure that the two sides of the board match up reasonably accurately. A board around 50 to 100 millimetres long is adequate, and the leads from the main circuit board can be soldered direct to the tracks of the board. This leaves a slight risk of the tracks being pulled away from the board, and it is probably worthwhile going to the expense of buying a 2 by 22 way 0.156 inch female edge connector and making the connections via this. Figure 10 gives details of the connections to the cartridge port.

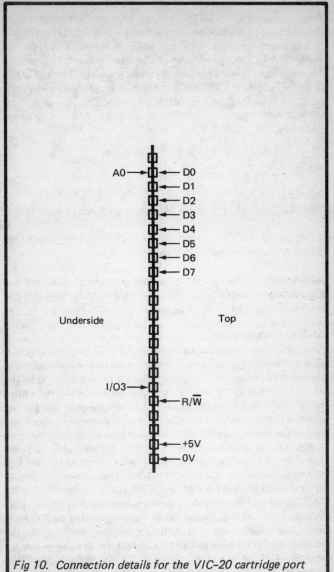

Fig 10. Connection details for the VIC-20 cartridge port

Software

Testing and using the MIDI input is difficult since the three byte groups of data will often be received over a period of time which is only about one thousanth of a second in duration. This is far too fast for BASIC to cope with, and either machine code or assembly language must be used instead. A rudimentary check can be made using this simple BASIC routine which transmits values and then reads them back again. The MIDI IN and MIDI OUT sockets of the interface must, of course, be linked before this test program will work.

```
5 REM VIC MIDI TEST PROG
10 INPUT A
20 POKE 39936,A
30 IF (PEEK(39937) AND 128)=0 THEN 30
40 PRINT PEEK(39936)
50 POKE 39937,0
60 GOTO 10
```

The first value is entered at line 10, and then it is transmitted from the MIDI output at line 20. Note that the values must be integers in the range 0 to 255. Line 30 provides a hold-off until the Data Received output goes high to indicate that a byte of data has been received. The operating speed of BASIC is such that line 30 may well be superfluous in this case, but in practical applications a test of the Data Received flag will always be needed before a reading is taken in order to avoid multiple readings. The method used in this program is to logic AND the value from the interface with 128. The purpose of this is to effectively eliminate D0 to D6 and to read only D7. This gives a returned value of 0 if D7 is low, or 128 if it is high, and the states of the other seven bits have no effect whatever on the returned value. Most microprocessors have logic AND instructions, and a machine code equivalent of line 30 should not be difficult to devise. An alternative way of testing the Data received flag is to check whether or not the returned value is greater than 127. It will always be greater than 127 if the flag is high, but 127 or less if it is not.

The value read from the interface is printed on the screen at line 40, and this should, of course, be the same value that was entered at line 10. Line 50 clears the Data Received flag, and then line 60 loops the program back to line 10 so that the next number can be entered. Use RUN/STOP – RESTORE to break out of the program.

CBM 64

It is possible to use the interface with the Commodore 64 computer without altering the circuit in any way. There is a slight change mechanically in that connections to the cartridge port of the Commodore 64 are made by way of a 2 by 22 way 0.1 inch male edge connector (and not a 0.156 inch type). As for the VIC-20, a suitable connector can be made up from a piece of double-sided copper clad board using normal printed circuit construction techniques. In fact the interface could be constructed on a double-sided printed circuit board designed to plug into the cartridge port. In practice the design and construction of a suitable board could be quite difficult, and this system is not always very reliable with medium to large size boards. Any tension on the connecting leads or vibration tending to disrupt the connections between the board and the computer, and this can result in problems with the computer crashing. It is probably easier and better to house the unit in a small metal or plastic box, with the printed circuit board connected to the cartridge port via a length of ribbon cable and the appropriate type of connector. The connections to the cartridge port of the Commodore 64 are slightly different to those for the VIC-20, and the correct method of connection is given in Figure 11. The main difference is that line I/O2 is used in place of I/O3. This places the interface at addresses from 57088 to 57343. Assuming the base addresses are used, the interface is controlled using addresses 57088 and 57089, as detailed below:-

Read 57088	Read received values
Write 57088	Transmit values
Read 57089	Read Data Received flag
Write 57089	Reset Data Received flag

The VIC-20 test program described previously can be used with the Commodore 64 simply by changing address 39936 to 57088, and address 39937 to 57089.

When the interface is used with the Commodore 64 or BBC model B computer it is possible to derive the 500kHz clock signal from the computer's clock signal. The 02 clock signal of the Commodore 64 is at a frequency of 980kHz, which when divided by two gives a 490kHz signal. This is close enough to the ideal frequency of 500kHz to give good results. The clock of the BBC computer runs at 2MHz, but it is effectively slowed down for 1MHz for input/output devices (hence the expansion port of the BBC machine has been called the "1MHz Bus"). When divided by

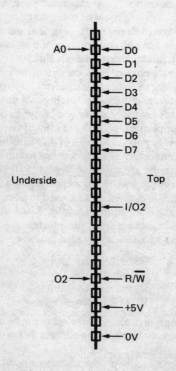

A0 → D0
→ D1
→ D2
→ D3
→ D4
→ D5
→ D6
→ D7

Underside   Top

→ I/O2

O2 →   ← R/W̄

← +5V

← 0V

Fig 11. Connection details for the CBM64 cartridge port

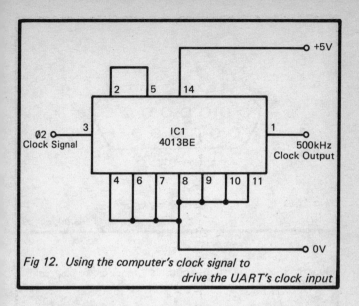

Fig 12. Using the computer's clock signal to drive the UART's clock input

two this signal obviously provides precisely the required clock frequency of 500kHz.

A suitable divide by two circuit is provided in Figure 12, and this is just one section of a 4013BE dual D type flip/flop with the appropriate method of connection. Unfortunately this method of clock generation will not work well with the VIC-20 computer which has a clock frequency of just over 1.1MHz. When divided by two this would give a frequency of over 550kHz, and an error of over 10% is too large to guarantee reliable operation.

BBC Model B

On the face of it there is no difficulty in using the interface with the BBC model B computer's 1MHz Bus. The required data, address, and control lines are available, but there are, nevertheless, a couple of problems. The simplest one to overcome is the lack of any power supply output on the 1MHz bus. There are 5 volt outputs on the user port, power port, and the analogue port though. In practice the analogue port is probably the easiest one to use as the take off point, and Figure 13 shows which pin to use. Connection to the analogue port is by way of a 15 way D type plug. As only one connection has to be made in this case it is possible to

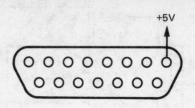

+5V

Fig 13. A +5 volt supply can be taken from the BBC computer's analogue port

adopt the cheaper alternative of using a 1 millimetre plug, taking due care to always fit this into the appropriate position in the D socket.

The second problem is with the page select lines of the computer (the BBC computer's equivalents of I/O2 and I/O3 in the Commodore machines). These are lines FC and FD, and they pulse low when any address from &FC00 to &FCFF and &FD00 to &FDFF are accessed, very much like their equivalents in the Commodore machines. There is a difference though, and this is brought about by the use of a 2MHz clock for memory operations, and a 1MHz clock for input/output operations. It can result in faulty operation unless steps are taken to clean up the pulses from the page select lines. There are various ways of doing this, but fortunately the 6402 only seems to require the most basic of clean-up circuits. A suitable circuit is shown in Figure 14, and this just consists of three NOR gates from a 74LS02 device connected in a suitable configuration.

Connections to the 1MHz Bus are made via a 34 way IDC header socket as shown in Figure 15. It is probably easiest to buy the socket ready-fitted with a length of ribbon cable, and to simply ignore the leads that are not required.

The interface appears at addresses from &FC00 to &FCFF, and again assuming the base addresses are to be used, it is controlled in the manner detailed as follows:-

34

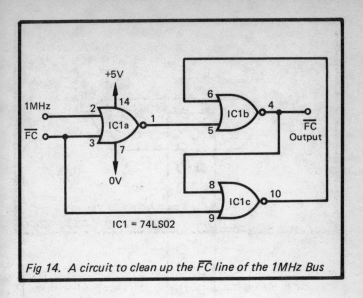

Fig 14. A circuit to clean up the $\overline{FC}$ line of the 1MHz Bus

Read &FC00	Read received values
Write &FC00	Transmit values
Read &FC01	Read Data Received flag
Write &FC01	Reset Data Received flag

The method of testing suggested for the Commodore machines is easily applied to the BBC machine, and a suitable test program follows:-

```
5 REM BBC MIDI TEST PROG
10 INPUT A
20 ?&FC00=A
30 IF (?&FC01 AND 128)=0 THEN 30
40 PRINT ?&FC00
50 ?&FC01=0
60 GOTO 10
```

Spectrum

The Sinclair Spectrum is a very different prospect as far as interfacing is concerned, and it is Z80 based whereas the Commodore 64, VIC-20, and BBC model B computers are all

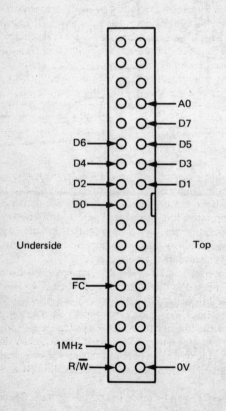

Fig 15. The connections to the 1MHz Bus
of the BBC Model B computer

based on the 6502 microprocessor (or a 6502 derivative). The Sinclair Spectrum does not provide an equivalent of the page select or I/O lines of the Commodore and BBC machines.

On the other hand, the method of input/output interfacing adopted by Sinclair for the Spectrum·computer still makes it relatively easy to interface user add-ons to the expansion port. Normally with a Z80 based computer the eight least significant address lines (A0 to A7) are used for input/output operations, and they are decoded to provide up to 256 input/output addresses. Unlike 6502 based computers, the input/output circuits are not memory mapped, but are instead in a separate input/output map. Two control lines are used to provide the separate maps, and these are IORQ (input/output request) and MEMRQ (memory request). The former goes low while the microprocessor is performing an input/output operation, and the latter goes low while a memory access is being performed.

The Spectrum has a somewhat simplified scheme of operation which makes adding circuits to the expansion port very much easier than it might otherwise be. For input/output operations all sixteen address lines are utilized, and a device is activated by taking the appropriate address line low. Spare address lines can be brought into operation where an input/output circuit requires several addresses. Address line A5 is free for user add-ons, and lines A6 and A7 can also be used if required.

In order to interface a device to the expansion port it must therefore be connected so that it is activated when IORQ and A5 both go low. Additionally, A6 and (or) A7 can be used where more than one address is required (as in this case). The Z80 does not have a read/write line like the 6502, but instead it has separate read (RD) and write (WR) lines. The read line goes low during read operations – the write line goes low during write operations. Obviously the decoder circuit must also process the WR and RD lines.

The MIDI interface can be made to operate with the Spectrum computer by altering the connections to IC2, the 3 to 8 line decoder. This modification is shown in Figure 16.

In this circuit the decoder has all three address inputs used, but still only four of the outputs are needed. The two negative enable inputs are utilized, and they are fed from IORQ and address line A5. Remember it is these going low that must activate the interface. The positive enable input of IC2 is not required and is simply tied to the +5 volt rail. Address line A6 plus the read and

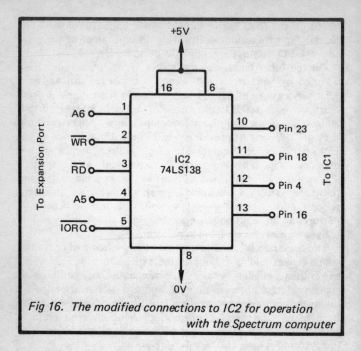

Fig 16. The modified connections to IC2 for operation with the Spectrum computer

write lines are decoded by the three address inputs of IC2. As only two addresses are required it is not necessary to decode A7 as well.

By using the correct outputs of IC2 the interface can be controlled in the manner detail below:-

Read 65503	Read received values
Write 65503	Transmit values
Read 65439	Read Data Received flag
Write 65439	Reset Data Received flag

Connections to the expansion port of the Spectrum are made by way of a 2 by 28 way 0.1 inch female edge connector fitted with a polarising key in the appropriate position. Edge connectors for the Spectrum, complete with polarising key, are readily available. Details of the required connections to the port are provided in Figure 17. Incidentally, there is a clock signal available at the

38

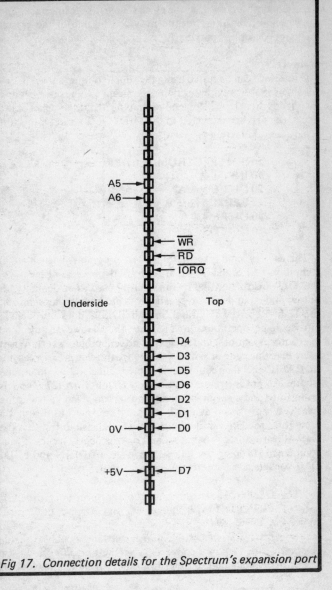

Fig 17. Connection details for the Spectrum's expansion port

Spectrum's expansion port, but this is an intermittent signal which is consequently unusable as the clock source for the interface. The clock signal must therefore be provided by one of the crystal oscillators described previously.

Software

The interface can be tested using the simple routine shown below which, as in the previous examples, transmits values to itself and then reads them back. Remember that the MIDI IN socket of the interface must be connected to the MIDI OUT socket if this test program is to function properly.

```
5 REM SPECTRUM TEST PROG
10 INPUT A
20 OUT 65503,A
30 PRINT IN 65503
40 OUT 65439,0
50 GO TO 10
```

This is very similar to the other test programs, but with Z80 computers PEEK and POKE are only used for accessing memory. The OUT instruction and IN function are used when dealing with output and input devices respectively. The program does not test the Data Received flag, and Sinclair BASIC does not include bitwise logic operations to facilitate this. However, the Z80 microprocessor does, and so there is no real problem here. When using machine code or assembly language this flag is easily tested. In BASIC the flag could be tested by checking to determine whether or not the returned value was greater than 127. There is no need to add a check into the test program given above as the relatively slow speed at which the program runs ensures that a premature reading can not be taken. If you wish to test that the Data Received flag is being set and reset properly try these four commands (keeping the link between the MIDI IN and MIDI OUT sockets of the interface).

```
OUT 65503,0
PRINT IN 65439
OUT 65439,0
PRINT IN 65439
```

The first command transmits a value which should be received on the MIDI input, causing the Data Received flag to be set. The next command reads the flag, and should return a value of 128 or more. The third instruction resets the flag. Note that the value written to input/output address 65439 is irrelevant (although it must be a legal quantity) as it is the address decoder and not one of the data lines that is used to supply the reset pulse. The final command reads the Data Received flag again, and it should return a value of less than 128.

Step-time sequencing can be achieved in much the same way as for the Commodore machines and the BBC computer. This is the Spectrum equivalent of the basic step-time sequencer programs described earlier in this chapter.

```
5 REM SPECTRUM SEQUENCER PROG
10 READ A,B
15 IF A=0 THEN STOP
20 OUT 65503,150:OUT 65503,A:OUT 65503,127
30 FOR D=1 TO B:NEXT D
40 OUT 65503,134:OUT 65503,A:OUT 65503,0
50 GO TO 10
60 DATA  60,100,62,100,64,100,65,100,67,100,69,100,
71,100,72,200,0,0
```

This is very much the same as the previous sequencer programs, but obviously a few minor changes have had to be made in order to accommodate Sinclair BASIC and the different port address.

Amstrad CPC464

As far as interfacing is concerned the Amstrad CPC464 computer is very similar to the Sinclair Spectrum, and both machines are Z80 based. The Amstrad machine does not actually have an expansion port as such, but the "Floppy Disc" port is eminently suitable for add-on devices as it provides all the necessary address, data, and control lines, plus supply and other useful lines. Like the Spectrum, the Amstrad CPC464 utilizes a simplied form of input/output address mapping which enables user add-ons to be easily intefaced to it. A10 going low is used to activate user add- ons, rather like A5 in the Spectrum's scheme of things. Where more than one address is needed the eight least significant address lines (A0 to A7) can be decoded as well. A10 low corresponds to an address range of &F800 to &FBFF (some 1k). With an

41

unexpanded machine it seems to be perfectly alright to use any addresses within this range, but with a disc drive fitted Amstrad recommend that only addresses in the range &F8E0 to &F8FF, &F9E0 to &F9FF, &FAE0 to &FAFF, and &FBE0 to &FBFF should be utilized. In other words the number on address lines A0 to A7 should be in the range &E0 to &FF. This avoids user add-ons causing any inteference with the disc drives or other peripherals, or vice versa.

Provided no disc drive or other peripheral devices are fitted to the computer it is quite easy to fit the MIDI interface to the floppy disc port, and Figure 18 shows the necessary modification to the circuit. This is very similar to the system of decoding used for the Spectrum, with A10 being connected instead of A5, and A0 being connected in place of A6. The interface appears as echoes throughout the &F800 to &FBFF address range, but if the base addresses are used when using the interface it is controlled in the

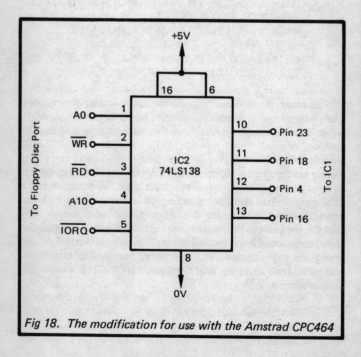

Fig 18. The modification for use with the Amstrad CPC464

manner shown below:-

Read &F800	Read Received Data flag
Write &F800	Reset Received Data flag
Read &F801	Read Received values
Write &F801	Transmit values

A 2 by 25 way 0.1 inch pitch female edge connector is needed to make the connections to the disc port, and the necessary connections are shown in Figure 19. The computer's connector has provision for a polarising key, but it may not be possible to find a matching edge connector. If it is not, it might be possible to add one to an ordinary 2 by 25 way connector, or the simple alternative of clearly marking the top and bottom edges of the connector will suffice.

The CPC464 has a 4MHz clock signal which is available at the floppy disc port (see Figure 19). This can be used as the basis of the 500kHz clock generator for the UART, and all that is needed is a three stage binary (divide by eight) counter circuit, as shown in Figure 20.

Software

A point worth emphasizing is that add-ons should always be connected to the computer prior to switch-on, not afterwards. This is especially the case with circuits that connect direct to the computer's busses, where at best the computer is likely to crash when the add-on is connected, and at worst the computer, the add-on, or both could be damaged. When any of the MIDI interfaces described in this book are fitted to the computer, after switch-on the usual start-up routine should always be obtained. If it is not there is almost certainly a fault in the interface, and the computer should be switched off again at once, after which the interface should be thoroughly checked for errors.

As in the previous examples, a good way of initially testing the interface is to get it to transmit values to itself and then read them back. A suitable test program is provided below. If all is well this will only work when the MIDI IN and MIDI OUT sockets are coupled together.

```
5 REM CPC464 TEST PROG
10 INPUT A
20 OUT &F801,A
```

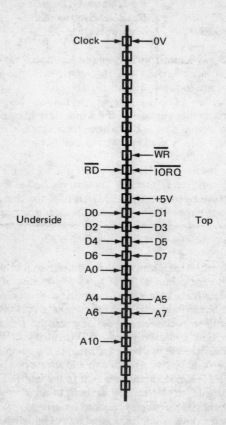

Clock → ← 0V

WR̄
R̄D → ← ĪŌRQ̄

← +5V
D0 → ← D1
D2 → ← D3
D4 → ← D5
D6 → ← D7
A0 →

Underside

Top

A4 → ← A5
A6 → ← A7

A10 →

Fig 19. The connections to the CPC464's
"Floppy Disc" port

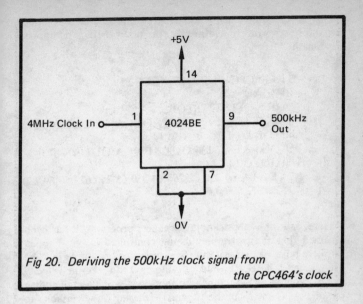

Fig 20. Deriving the 500kHz clock signal from the CPC464's clock

```
30 PRINT INP(&F801)
40 GOTO 10
```

This operates in much the same way as the previous test programs, but note that the CPC464 uses the INP function when reading input devices, and not IN, as used by the Spectrum and some other Z80 based computers.

These four commands can be used to check that the Data Received flag can be read and reset properly. Again, the MIDI IN and MIDI OUT sockets of the interface must be linked if this test routine is to function properly.

```
OUT &F801,0
PRINT INP(&F800) AND 128
OUT &F800,0
PRINT INP(&F800) AND 128
```

If everything is functioning properly this should give a returned value of 128 from the second command (flag set), and 0 from the fourth (flag reset).

This basic step-time sequencer program can be used to test out the interface with a synthesiser or other MIDI equipped instrument.

```
5 REM CPC464 SEQUENCER PROG
10 READ A,B
20 IF A=0 THEN STOP
30 OUT &F801,150:OUT &F801,A:OUT &F801,127
40 FOR D=1 TO B:NEXT
50 OUT &F801,134:OUT &F801,A:OUT &F801,0
60 GOTO 10
70 DATA  60,250,62,250,64,250,65,250,67,250,69,250,
71,250,72,500,0,0
```

Here, as in the other simple sequencer programs, it has been assumed that the instrument being controlled is not a touch sensitive type, or that it is but the same velocity values are to be used for each note. It would be quite easy to make the velocity values programmable though, and this would only entail adding parameters C and D at line 10, and then using these variables to replace the dummy velocity values at lines 30 and 50.

Amstrad CPC6128

The CPC464 MIDI interface might function properly with the Amstrad disc drive added to the machine, but there is a problem here. The same is also true of the CPC664 computer (which is basically a CPC464 with built-in disc drive), and the CPC6128 (which is more or less a CPC664 with an extra 64k of memory). As pointed out earlier, by using addresses in the range &F8E0 to &F8FF the interface can be controlled without any risk of interfering with operation of the disc drive, or other Amstrad peripherals such as the communications port. However, when any external add-ons are accessed line A10 is taken low, and this would almost certainly cause spurious operations of the MIDI interface.

This can be avoided by decoding some of the eight least significant address lines so that the interface is only activated when addresses in the area reserved for user add-ons are accessed. This is easily accomplished, and all that is needed is a couple of extra gates connected as shown in Figure 21. These are the two 4 input NAND gates of a 74LS20 device, and one of them is fed

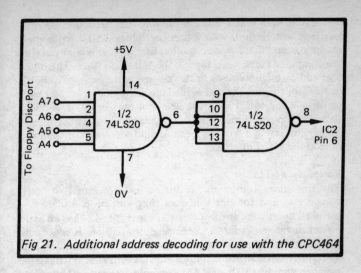

Fig 21. Additional address decoding for use with the CPC464

from lines A4 to A7. This gate's output will go low only when all four inputs are high (which corresponds to the hexadecimal digit "F"). The second gate is just wired as an inverter, so that the output of the circuit goes high when all four inputs are high. This output is used to drive the positive enable input of IC2 in the interface, which is the 3 to 8 line decoder. This input was previously unused and therefore tied to the positive supply rail. This places the interface at addresses from &F8F0 to &F8FF (and corresponding addresses in pages &F9, &FA, and &FB), which is the upper half section of memory which is reserved for user add-ons. When using the additional address decoding the addresses shown below are used to control the interface.

Read &F8F0	Read Data Received flag
Write &F8F0	Reset Data Received flag
Read &F8F1	Read received values
Write &F8F1	Transmit values

It is only fair to point out that I have not had an opportunity to try out the interface with a CPC464 connected to a disc drive, or to one of the Amstrad machines which has a built-in disc drive. However, with the interface mapped into the Amstrad approved section of the input/output map there should be no difficulty with

47

any other peripherals interfering with the interface, or the interface interfering with other peripherals. There is one exception, and that is where another user add-on is connected to the computer at the same time as the MIDI interface. The other user add-on might be designed to only use addresses from &F8E0 to &F8EF, which is the half of the input/output map for user add-ons which the MIDI interface does not use. In this case there should be no problems. If the other device uses any addresses in the range &F8F0 to &F8FF, then it should not be used at the same time as the MIDI interface.

Enterprise 64/128

The Enterprise computers are further examples of Z80 based computers, and for our purposes they can be considered as identical apart from the fact that the Enterprise 128 has an extra 64k of memory. As far as interfacing user add-ons is concerned there is certainly no difference between the two machines. The Enterprise 128 is an attractive machine for MIDI use as it has good graphics and over 100k of RAM available to the user. This would enable excellent composer style programs to be produced by anyone with the requisite programming skills.

The system of input/output mapping adopted for the Enterprise computers is the standard Z80 type, with address lines A0 to A7 being decoded (together with IORQ) to give 256 input/output addresses from 0 to 255. On the face of it this makes it impossible to interface the MIDI interface unit to these computers without including some extra address decoding. In practice this is not necessary due to the way the internal input/output devices are fitted into the input/output map. All the internal circuits have addresses of 128 or more. This means that address line A7 is always high when an internal input/output device is being accessed, and user add-ons can simply be designed to operate when A7 and IORQ go low. This places user add-ons at addresses from 0 to 127. Obviously this method of interfacing is effectively the same as that adopted in the Sinclair Spectrum, except that address line A7 is used in place of A5. Also, where more than one input/output address is required lines A0 to A6 are all available, rather than just A6 and A7.

The interface can be connected to the Enterprise computers using the modified method of connection shown in Figure 22. This differs from the method used for the Sinclair Spectrum only in that A7 is connected in place of A5, and A0 is connected in place of

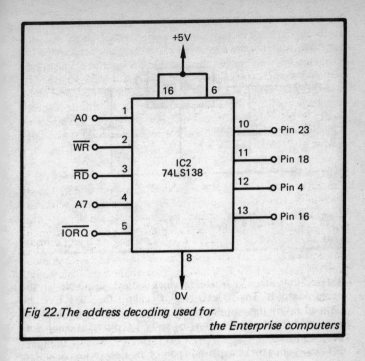

Fig 22.The address decoding used for
the Enterprise computers

A6. Once again assuming that the base addresses are to be used, the interface is controlled in the following manner:-

Read 0	Read Data Received flag
Write 0	Reset Data Received flag
Read 1	Read received values
Write 1	Transmit values

There is a slight problem when using the Enterprise expansion port in that no +5 volt supply output is provided. However, an unregulated +9 voly supply is available, and this can be used to power the circuit via the simple regulator circuit of Figure 23. This is just a small (100 milliamp) 5 volt (positive) monolithic voltage regulator plus a couple of decoupling capacitors to aid good stability. The decoupling capacitors should be mounted physically close to the regulator as they might otherwise be ineffective.

The system clock frequency of the Enterprise computers is

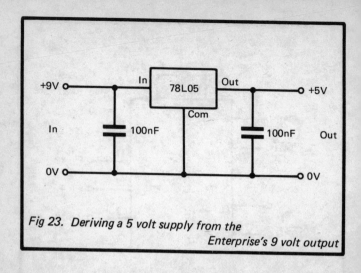

Fig 23. Deriving a 5 volt supply from the
Enterprise's 9 volt output

4MHz, but there is a 1MHz clock output available at the
expansion port. The 500kHz clock signal for the UART can be
derived from this using exactly the same method that was
suggested for the Commodore 64 and BBC model B computers
(see Figure 12).

Connections to the expansion port of the Enterprise computers
are made via a 2 by 33 way 0.1 inch pitch female edge connector. If
a type having the required number of ways proves to be
impossible to obtain it is not too difficult to cut down a larger type
to the correct number of ways using a hacksaw. There is no
provision for a polarising key in the computer's connector (this is
effectively provided by the casing which surrounds the
connector). Rather than trying to improvise some form of
polarising system it is probably better to just label the top and
bottom edges of accordingly. Details of the connections to the
port are shown in Figure 24.

Software

Using our previous methods of testing, with values being
transmitted from the MIDI OUT socket, received at the MIDI IN
socket, and printed on-screen, this simple test program is suitable.

5 REM ENTERPRISE TEST PROG

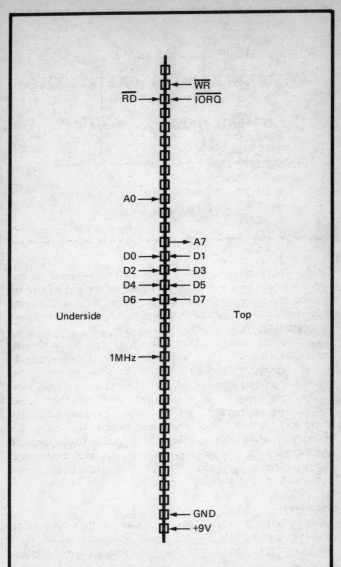

Fig 24. The connections to the Enterprise expansion port

```
10 INPUT A
20 OUT 1,A
30 PRINT IN(1)
40 GOTO 10
```

The Enterprise version of the basic step-time sequencer is given below:-

```
5 REM ENTERPRISE SEQUENCER PROG
10 READ A,B
20 IF A=0 THEN STOP
30 OUT 1,150
40 OUT 1,A
50 OUT 1,127
60 FOR D=1 TO B
70 NEXT
80 OUT 1,134
90 OUT 1,A
100 OUT 1,0
110 GOTO 10
120 DATA 60,200,62,200,64,200,65,200,67,200,69,200,
71,400,0,0
```

To check the Data Received flag these four commands can be used:-

```
OUT 1,0
PRINT IN(0)
OUT 0,0
PRINT IN(0)
```

This should give a value of 255 from the second command, and a value of 127 from the fourth. Remember to link the MIDI OUT to the MIDI IN for this test.

MSX

The MSX computers, as far as interfacing is concerned, are virtually identical to the Enterprise machines. They use standard Z80 interfacing with all the internal circuits at addresses greater than 127. There are minor differences, and one is the inclusion of a +5 volt output which renders the use of an external regulator circuit unnecessary. Also, the clock output is at a frequency of

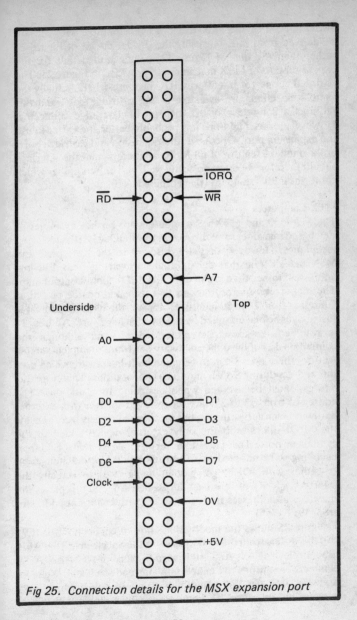

Fig 25. Connection details for the MSX expansion port

4MHz. Of course, the 500MHz clock signal for the UART can still be derived from this, but using the divider circuit of Figure 20 rather than the one of Figure 12. Connection details for the expansion port of MSX machines are provided in Figure 25. The required connector is a 50 way IDC header socket. Actually the same connections are available at the cartridge port, and this requires a 2 by 25 way 0.1 inch pitch male edge connector. However, for user add-ons it is probably better and easier to use the expansion port. Of course, the expansion and cartridge ports are a standard feature of all MSX computers, and the interface should therefore operate perfectly well with any computer which conforms to this standard (the Toshiba HX10, etc.).

MTX Computers

The MTX500 and MTX512 computers are further examples of Z80 based machines, and they again use standard Z80 interfacing techniques. However, they are different to the Enterprise and MSX machines in that the internal hardware is placed at low addresses, rather than in the upper half of the input/output map. The manufacturers recommend that user add-ons be placed at addresses from 16 to 30 inclusive, which is the block of addresses just above the one occupied by the internal hardware. Address 31 is reserved for cassette remote control, and although the computers do not have the necessary hardware to implement this feature, there does seem to be some built-in sofware which uses this address during SAVE and LOAD operations. Therefore this address must be avoided when designing user add-ons. The addresses from 32 to 255 are all reserved for use with external hardware such as disc drives, but these are obviously free for use if the MIDI interface is the only external device added to the expansion port. This permits a very simple system of address decoding to be adopted, with address line A6 or A7 going high (together with IORQ going low) being used to activate the interface. Here we are using address line A6, and this places the interface at addresses from 64 to 127 (with echoes at addresses from 191 to 255).

Figure 26 shows the modified method of connection for IC2, and this differs from the system used for the Spectrum in that A6 is used in place of A5, And A0 is used in place of A6. Also, A6 is connected to the positive enable input instead of a negative enable input, as it is this line going high rather than low which must activate the interface. The unused negative enable input is, of

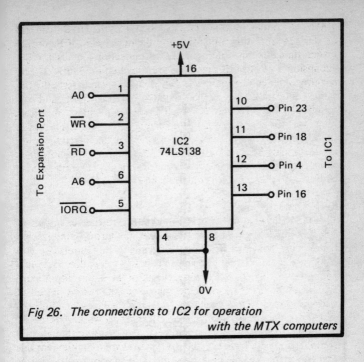

Fig 26. The connections to IC2 for operation
with the MTX computers

course, tied to the negative supply rail. This method of decoding
places the interface at these addresses:-

Read 64	Read Data Received flag
Write 64	Reset Data Received flag
Read 65	Read received values
Write 65	Transmit values

The expansion port of the MTX computers requires a 2 by 30
way 0.1 inch pitch edge connector, and there is provision for a
polarising key. In practice it is probably best to use a 2 by 28 way
type fitted with a polarising key, as used for the Sinclair Spectrum.
Obviously this does not permit connections to be made to all the
terminals of the expansion port, but those which are not reached
are not required in this application anyway. The polarising key
avoids the risk of fitting the connector up-side-down, and a
further advantage of the Spectrum type is that it is likely to be

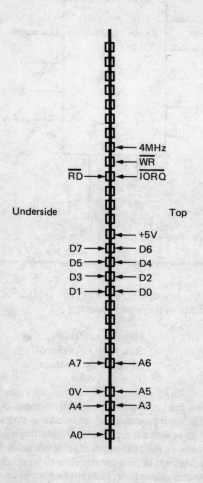

Underside

Top

4MHz
WR
RD → ← IORQ

+5V
D7 → ← D6
D5 → ← D4
D3 → ← D2
D1 → ← D0

A7 → ← A6

0V → ← A5
A4 → ← A3

A0 →

Fig 27. The connections to the MTX expansion port

56

much more readily obtainable (and probably cheaper as well). Connection details for the MTX expansion port are given in Figure 27, and this assumes that a 2 by 28 way connector is used.

Software

The test routines for the MTX version of the interface are given below, and they are exact equivalents for those provided previously for other machines.

```
5 REM MTX TEST PROG
10 INPUT A
20 OUT 65,A
30 PRINT INP(65)
40 GOTO 10

5 REM MTX SEQUENCER PROG
10 READ A,B
20 IF A=0 THEN STOP
30 OUT 65,150:OUT 65,A:OUT 65,127
40 FOR D=1 TO B:NEXT
50 OUT 65,150:OUT 65,A:OUT 65,0
60 GOTO 10
70 DATA
60,300,62,300,64,300,65,300,67,300,69,300,71,300,72,
600,0,0

OUT 65,0
PRINT INP(64)
OUT 64,0
PRINT INP(64)
```

Further Decoding

The very basic method of address decoding suggested above is perfectly alright if the computer is not going to be used with disc drives or other external hardware which interfaces to the busses. If it is to be used while the disc drive or another input/output device is connected to the computer, then some further address decoding is required, and a suitable circuit is shown in Figure 28. This retains the 3 to 8 line decoder (IC2) from the original decoder circuit, but it is augmented by a 74LS32 quad 2 input OR gate. In this circuit only three of the gates are needed, and no connections are made to the fourth gate. The three gates that are utilized are in

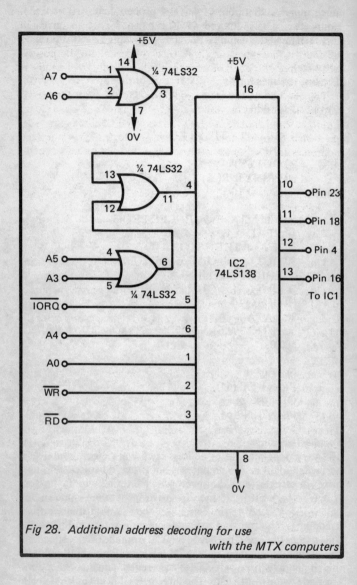

Fig 28. Additional address decoding for use
with the MTX computers

58

fact connected to form a 4 input OR gate which is used to decode address lines A3 and A5 to A7. This circuit feeds into a negative enable input of IC2, and IC2 can therefore only be activated when all four of these lines are low. Line A4 feeds into the positive enable input of IC2. In other respects the decoding is the same as in the original circuit.

This method of decoding places the interface at addresses 16 and 17, with echoes occuring at addresses up to 23. Obviously the interface should not be used at the same time as another user add-on which occupies any addresses from 16 to 23. If the base addresses are used the interface is controlled in the manner shown below:-

Read 16	Read Data Received flag
Write 16	Reset Data Received flag
Read 17	Read received values
Write 17	Transmit values

The test routines given earlier can obviously be used with the modified interface if the addresses are changed accordingly.

There is a 4MHz clock signal available on the expansion port of the MTX computers, and in conjunction with the divide-by-eight circuit of Figure 20 this can provide the 500kHz clock signal for the UART.

ZX81

The Sinclair ZX81 is perhaps considerably less than the ideal computer for MIDI use, especially in its unexpanded form where the amount of RAM available for program use and data storage is, to say the least, somewhat limited. On the other hand, there are a great many of these computers laying around unused, and if you do not have one already it would probably be possible to obtain one for a minimal monetary outlay. If you are not experienced at electronics and computer interfacing then a ZX81 represents a low cost and low risk introduction to the subject.

Interfacing to the ZX81 is usually somewhat unconventional due to some of the non-standard techniques used in the machine. In fact standard Z80 input/output techniques can be utilized, but there is a problem with this method in that the ZX81's version of BASIC does not include the OUT instruction or the IN (or INP) function. This makes it impossible to control a device in the input/output map from BASIC, although control using machine code would still be possible. However, as most users of ZX81 add-ons are likely to prefer the use of BASIC rather than machine code, initially at any rate, ZX81 add-ons are usually memory mapped. They can then be controlled using the POKE instruction and the PEEK function.

With its ROM and RAM chips of very limited capacity, the ZX81 has plenty of spare memory locations. There is a slight complication though in that the internal circuit uses less than full address decoding, so that echoes of the ROM occur throughout the address range. This does not mean that the echoes render the affected addresses unusable, as the ZX81 has a couple of unusual inputs on its expansion bus. These are ROMCS (ROM chip select) and RAMCS (RAM chip select). These can be taken to the high state to disable the ROM and RAM chips respectively, so that the echoes are suppressed and the internal hardware does not interfere with the operation of add-on circuits. These inputs must not just be held continuously in the high state as this would prevent the computer from operating. Neither should they be pulled low by an external circuit when it is not being activated. They must be taken high when the add-on is operated, and left floating at other times. In practice it is usually only ROMCS that needs to be controlled.

Figure 29 shows a suitable address decoder for use with the ZX81. This has similarities to the previous address decoder circuits, with a 74LS138 (IC2) decoding the A0, WR, and RD lines, and providing four outputs to drive control inputs of the UART. Some further decoding is required though, and this is provided by a second 74LS138 3 to 8 line decoder. This decodes address lines A13 to A15, plus the MREQ line. It drives one of IC2's negative enable inputs from output "O". The other negative enable input and the positive enable input of IC2 are not needed in this circuit and are just tied to the negative and positive supplies respectively.

Tr1 operates as an inverter which is driven from output "O" of IC3. A positive pulse is therefore generated at Tr1's collector each time the decoder is activated, and this is coupled to the ROMCS input of the ZX81 via D1. The latter enables Tr1 to pull the ROMCS input high, but it prevents it from taking it to the low state. This ensures that the computer is able to function normally when the interface is not being accessed. Figure 30 shows the connections to the ZX81 expansion port.

This system of address decoding places the interface at the

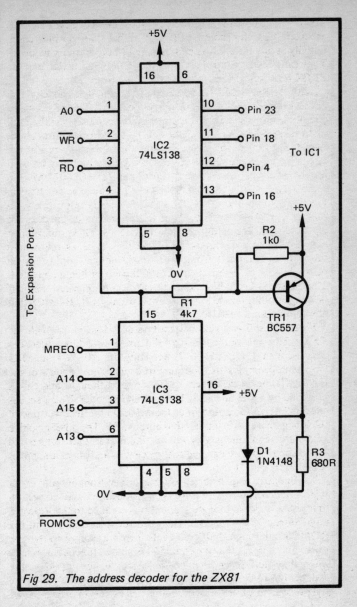

Fig 29. The address decoder for the ZX81

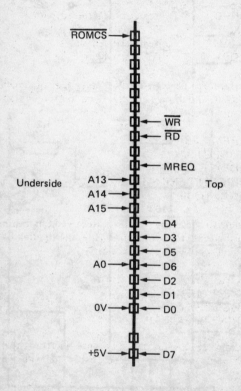

Fig 30. The connections to the ZX81 expansion port

addresses from 8192 to 16383. This part of the memory map is the one normally selected for ZX81 add-ons and it seems to work well with a ZX81 fitted with the 16k add-on RAMPACK as well as with an unexpanded machine. Once again assuming that the base addresses are to be used, the interface is controlled in this manner:-

Read 8192	Read Data Received flag
Write 8192	Reset Data Received flag
Read 8193	Read received values
Write 8193	Transmit values

The interface can be tested using the system of transmitting values to itself and then printing them on-screen, and this program is suitable.

```
5 REM ZX81 TEST PROG
10 INPUT A
20 POKE 8193,A
30 PRINT PEEK 8913
40 GO TO 10
```

It is possible to check that the Data Received flag can be read and reset using these four commands (keeping the link between the MIDI OUT and MIDI IN sockets).

```
POKE 8193,0
PRINT PEEK 8192
POKE 8192,0
PRINT PEEK 8192
```

This should return a value of 128 or more first (probably 255), and then a value of under 128 (probably 127) at the final command.

It is not possible to produce a direct ZX81 equivalent of the basic sequencer program as the ZX81 does not have the READ instruction and the DATA statement in its BASIC vocabulary. The alternative that has to be adopted is the use of arrays, as suggested on pages 145 and 146 of the ZX81 manual. This simple program can be used as a quick test of the interface with a synthesiser or other instrument. All it does is to switch on a note (middle C) for a second or two.

```
  5 ZX81 INSTRUMENT TEST PROG
 10 POKE 8913,150
 20 POKE 8913,60
 30 POKE 8913,127
 40 FOR D=1 TO 50
 50 NEXT D
 60 POKE 8913,134
 70 POKE 8913,60
 80 POKE 8913,0
 90 STOP
```

Sinclair QL

For MIDI applications the Sinclair QL is an attractive proposition as it offers a substantial amount of memory at relatively low cost. It also uses the advanced 68008 microprocessor, and together with a suitable assembler it would be possible to write good assembly language programs for MIDI step-time and real-time sequencing. The 68000 series of microprocessors mostly have 16 bit data busses, but the 68008 is a version which has an ordinary 8 bit type. It can therefore be interfaced to the MIDI port without too much difficulty.

The QL's expansion bus has a full range of inputs, outputs, and various other lines available. The 68000 microprocessors, like the 6502 and its derivatives, use memory mapped input/output devices. There is a great deal of unused memory space on the unexpanded QL, and it is not difficult to map user add-ons into unused areas. The QL has an address range of 1M, but only the lower 25% is used by an unexpanded machine. On the face of it this makes the necessary address decoding very simple, but in practice things are complicated by the fact that the QL's internal circuits seem to implement somewhat less than full address decoding. As a result of this it is probably best not to try adding devices into the unused upper 75% of the address range, much of which is reserved for QL peripherals etc. anyway. Instead, I prefer the method of mapping user add-ons into the part of the memory map which is reserved for the cartridge port. Obviously this precludes the simultaneous use of the MIDI interface and a cartridge, but it is unlikely that it would ever be necessary to use such a combination anyway.

The circuit of a suitable address decoder for the QL is shown in Figure 31. This is similar to the original circuit for the BBC and Commodore computers. Unfortunately though, the QL does not

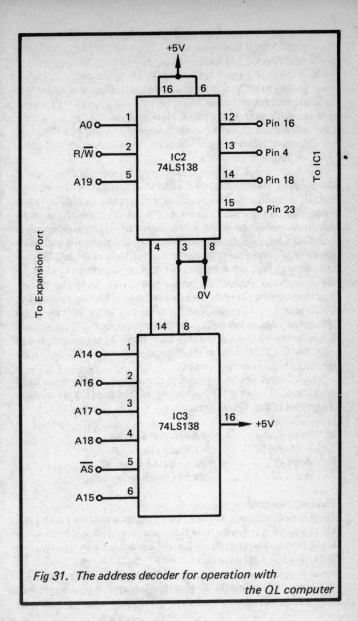

Fig 31. The address decoder for operation with
the QL computer

have a decoded output which activates whenever an address in the appropriate range is accessed. We therefore have to provide the additional decoding in the interface, and most of this is provided by IC3, a second 3 to 8 line decoder. IC2 is connected in much the same way as in the original circuit, the only difference being that its second negative enable input (which was previously unused) now decodes address line A19. Note that the QL, with its large address range, has some twenty address lines and not the more usual sixteen. IC3 decodes address lines A14 to A18, as well as the Address Strobe (AS) line.

The latter is not a standard microprocessor control line, and it simply goes low when a valid address is present on the address bus. By decoding this line we ensure that spurious output pulses from IC3 are avoided. It is not normally needed as most microprocessors only have facilities for synchronous data transfers, but the 68008 can also handle asynchronous data transfers. Asynchronous transfers are used where the 68008 (with its relatively high clock frequency) normally operates too fast for the peripheral device. By using handshake lines the micro-processor can be slowed down to a suitable operating speed. The 6402 seems to be able to operate reliably with the 68008 running at full speed, but if necessary the microprocessor can be slowed down during accesses of the interface simply by connecting pin 14 of IC3 to the VPA input of the expansion port via a 1N4148 diode (the cathode connects to pin 14).

This address decoder places the interface at addresses from 49152 to 65535, but if the base addresses are used the interface is controlled in the following manner:-

Read 49152	Read received values
Write 49152	Transmit values
Read 49153	Read Data Received flag
Write 49153	Reset Data Received flag

Making Connections

To make connections to the QL's expansion port a 64 way DIN 41612 socket is required, and these are now available from a few of the larger component retailers. There are actually two types of DIN 41612 64 way connector available, the "a+b rows", and "a+c rows" types. The full connector is a 96 way type having three rows of 32 pins each. With the 64 way type one row of pins is omitted, giving either closely spaced rows (a+b) or widely spaced rows (a+c). It is the narrow spaced a+b type that is required for the QL.

Fitting the connector to the expansion port is made rather difficult by the fact that the port is recessed deep into the computer. About the only way around this is to fit the connector onto the end of an extension board, so that the connector can be pushed right into the computer. Connections can either be made direct to the board, or preferably, the board should be fitted with another DIN 41612 connector, but a plug rather than a socket. If the connections from the interface are then terminated at a DIN 41612 socket, this can be connected to the plug which is brought out to the exterior of the computer by the extension board. The drawback of this method is that it requires three connectors, which makes it relatively expensive.

The extension board can be made from a piece of double-sided copper laminate board about 3.4 inches wide and 4 inches long. 32 copper strips on a 0.1 inch pitch running down the length of the board are required. The strips are required on both sides of the board, and the two sets of strips must obviously match up reasonably accurately. If you do not wish to etch your own extension board, a simple alternative which seems to work well in practice is to use two pieces of 0.1 inch pitch stripboard. These should each have 32 copper strips and should be about 4 inches long. They are glued back-to-back (copper sides facing outwards) using any good quality general purpose adhesive, and then the connector or connectors are soldered in place. Figure 32 gives details of the connections to the QL's expansion port.

Both the ZX81 and the QL have clock outputs on their expansion buses, but in the present application it is probably easier to use one of the clock generator circuits described earlier rather than to try to derive the 500kHz clock signal from one of these outputs. The QL does not have a +5 volt output on the expansion port, and although a +5 volt output is included at the cartridge port, it would probably be easier to derive a +5 volt supply from the +9 volt output of the expansion port rather than tap off the supply from the cartridge port. The regulator of Figure 23 is suitable for this purpose.

The software test routines for the QL are shown below. These are much the same as those given previously and they do not merit further comment here.

5 REM QL MIDI TEST PROG

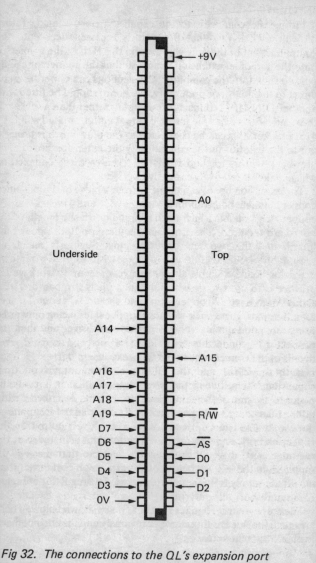

Fig 32. The connections to the QL's expansion port

```
10 CLS
20 INPUT A
30 POKE 49152,A
40 PRINT PEEK(49152)
50 GO TO 10
```

```
5 REM QL SEQUENCER PROG
7 RESTORE
10 READ A,B
20 IF A=0 THEN STOP
30 POKE 49152,150:POKE 49152,A:POKE 49152,127
40 FOR D=1 TO B:NEXT D
50 POKE 49152,134:POKE 49152,A:POKE 49152,0
60 GO TO 10
70 DATA 60,250,62,250,64,250,65,250,67,250,69,250,
71,250,72,500,0,0
```

```
POKE 49152,0
PRINT PEEK(49152)
POKE 49153,0
PRINT PEEK(49153)
```

Other Machines

Details of how to connect the interface to a wide range of popular
home computers have been provided, but obviously it is not
possible to include details of interfacing to all the numerous
machines that have been on sale in recent years. However, if the
buses of a computer are available at one of its ports, and there are
some spare memory or input/output addresses, then it should be
possible to connect the interface to it, although some extra
address decoding might be required. For example, the expansion
port of the Electron computer, as far as interfacing is concerned,
is very similar to the BBC model B's 1MHz Bus. However, the
two decoded page select lines are absent, and instead the
undecoded address lines A8 to A15 are provided. Interfacing
would therefore be much the same as for the BBC model B
computer, but with A8 to A15 being externally decoded to
provide a page select line for page &FC. Some computers provide
a regular clock output that can conveniently be divided down to
provide the 500kHz clock signal for the UART, but where there is
any doubt about the suitability of the clock output signal the
interface can be provided with its own crystal clock circuit.

Chapter 3

MIDI/CV INTERFACING

While MIDI undoubtedly has great advantages over the old gate/ CV system, it does have a minor drawback in that it can not be easily interfaced to non-MIDI equipment. With the gate/CV system there can be problems with incompatibility between various makes of instrument, in particular the gate signal requirements are far from standardised. In most cases interfacing one instrument to another requires nothing more than a simple interface to process the gate signals and produce compatible outputs (although some combinations of instrument may prove to be more awkward). There are only two control voltage standards, the old linear type, and the more recent logarithmic variety. Most of the instruments around these days are of the logarithmic type, and therefore give no problem with CV interfacing. Whatever the precise nature of the control voltage and gate output signals, they are in a form which is easily handled, and can, for example, be easily used to control home constructed equipment such as drum synthesisers and other percussion synthesisers. The purely digital nature of MIDI makes it far more difficult to use with home constructed equipment and, of course, it can not be directly interfaced to any form of gate/CV input.

In this chapter the topic of interfacing MIDI equipment to non-MIDI equipment will be covered. It is perfectly feasable to provide both MIDI to analogue and analogue to MIDI conversion, but the former is far more useful than the latter. MIDI to analogue conversion allows home constructed equipment to be added into a MIDI system, and it also permits an analogue synthesiser (or synthesisers) to be added to the set-up. If you have a good quality analogue synthesiser it will be capable of producing some excellent sounds, including some first rate percussive sounds. Such an instrument can be an extremely worthwhile addition to a MIDI set-up, either for lead use or to provide a percussion accompaniment. Even if you do not own a good quality analogue synthesiser, you may well be able to obtain one at quite low cost, and doing so would probably be well worthwhile.

Analogue to MIDI conversion is not particularly useful as this

70

would only be used with an analogue instrument acting as the MIDI controller, which would be an unlikely and rather idiosyncratic way of arranging things. It is somthing that could be achieved using a computer to read information from the synthesiser and then transmit the corresponding MIDI codes, but this would not, on the face of it at any rate, be worth the considerable effort involved, and it is not a subject that will be persued further in this book.

Gate Conversion

The first requirement for a MIDI to analogue converter is to generate gate pulses from the MIDI note-on and note-off information. In order to do this the MIDI serial signals must first be decoded into ordinary parallel 8 bit codes. Some simple logic circuitry is then all that is needed in order to translate the received codes into gate pulses. The circuit could operate in the onni mode, with gate pulses being generated regardless of which MIDI channel they are transmitted on, but in a practical set-up this is not likely to be of tremendous value. In most cases the analogue equipment will either need to play along with one channel of the MIDI equipment, or it will be assigned its own channel, giving the MIDI set-up an extra channel (provided at least one of the sixteen MIDI channels is free). It is being assumed here that only one channel will be used, but it is in fact possible to have several analogue instruments with each one having its own MIDI channel. Anyway, practically any realistic set-up is going to require the converter to operate in the mono mode, so that it responds to information on just one channel, or perhaps so that it provides several outputs with each one operating on a separate MIDI channel.

Figure 33 shows the circuit diagram for a MIDI to gate pulse converter, and this is based on the 6402 industry standard UART. As in the previous circuits, the programming inputs and the Control Register Load input are tied to the appropriate logic levels for the required eight data bits, one stop bit, and no parity word format. In this case only the receiver section of the device is utilized, and the Receiver Clock input at pin 17 must be fed with a 500kHz clock signal. No clock circuit is shown in Figure 33, but one of the clock generator circuits described in Chapter 2 will suffice. IC1 is the opto-isolator at the input of the circuit.

The eight bit output of IC2 is processed by two 4 to 16 line decoders (IC3 and IC4). IC3 processes the least significant nibble

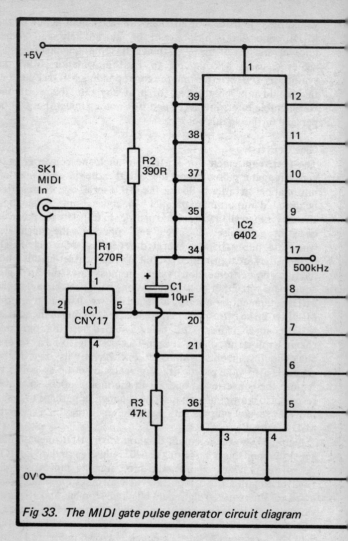

Fig 33. The MIDI gate pulse generator circuit diagram

(bits 0 to 3), while IC4 handles the most significant nibble (bits 4 to 7). Starting with IC4, this must recognise the note-on and note-off codes, which are (in binary) 1001 and 1000 respectively. There is a slight complication here in that some synthesisers, for reasons that

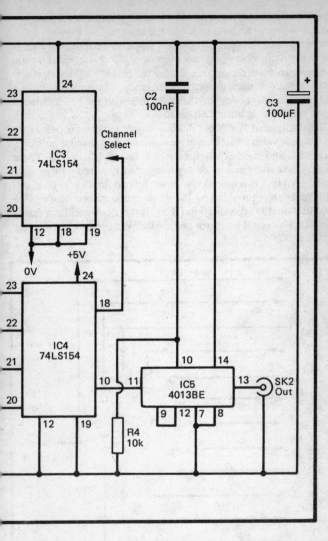

are less than obvious, transmit the same header code when a note is released as when a note is commenced (1001). My SCI Six-Tracks falls into this catagory, and the circuit has therefore been designed to only respond to the 1001 header code and to ignore the 1000 header code. We will consider ways of modifying the circuit to recognise both codes a little later in this chapter.

Output 9 of IC4 (pin 10) goes low when the 1001 header code is present on the most significant outputs of IC2. Note that this code only occurs on these outputs during the first byte of note-on and note-off information groups. Other types of information have a different header code, and the bytes following the header always have the most significant bit set to 0.

The output of IC4 is not directly usable as the gate pulse as it merely provides a brief negative pulse when a note-on header is received, and another when a note-off header is received. These pulses have to be processed to produce the required positive gate pulse. All that is required is a divide by two flip/flop circuit, and this function is provided by IC5. This is one section of a CMOS 4013BE dual D type flip/flop (IC5). If the clock oscillator based on a 1MHz crystal oscillator and a 4013BE is used, IC5 can be the

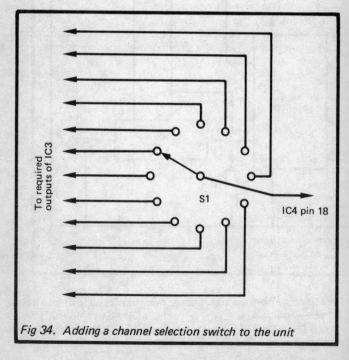

Fig 34. Adding a channel selection switch to the unit

unused section of the 4013BE. C2 and R4 provide a reset pulse to the circuit at switch-on so that the Q output is initially in the low state. It is from Q output that the gate signal is obtained incidentally. The first pulse from IC4 toggles the Q output high, the next one toggles it low again. This gives the required action with the Q output going high after a note-on header has been received, and low again when the accompanying note-off header is received.

If operation in the omni mode is all that is required then pin 18 of IC4 (one of its negative enable inputs) should simply be connected to the negative supply rail. For mono operation this pin must be fed from one of the outputs of IC3. This decodes the least significant nibble which contains the channel value, and it enables IC4 when the correct channel value is detected. It will sometimes happen that a note or velocity value will cause the appropriate output of IC3 to be triggered and activate IC4. This is of no consequence as on these occasions the most significant nibble will not be correct, and will not activate output 10 of IC4.

The interface can be assigned to any MIDI channel by selecting the appropriate output of IC3, and the table that follows gives details of channel numbers and their corresponding outputs.

MIDI CHANNEL	IC3 OUTPUT	/PIN No.
1	0	1
2	1	2
3	2	3
4	3	4
5	4	5
6	5	6
7	6	7
8	7	8
9	8	9
10	9	10
11	10	11
12	11	13
13	12	14
14	13	15
15	14	16
16	15	17

If you require the ability to select one of several channels, then all that is required is a switch connected as shown in Figure 34.

This is a twelve way type which therefore gives a choice of twelve channels. This should be more than adequate in practice, although it would be possible to have all sixteen channels available if a sixteen way switch was to be used. A sixteen way switch could probably prove to be impossible to obtain though. Note that the switch should be a break-before-make type, and not a make-before-break type (which would short circuit two outputs of IC3 together each time the switch was operated).

If you need the circuit to respond to header codes 1000 and 1001, then the easiest way of achieving this is to simply disconnect pin 23 of IC4 from pin 8 of IC2, and connect it to the positive supply rail instead. Bit 4 is then no longer decoded, and codes 1000 and 1001 will both activate the unit. If this method is used it is possible to use the (cheaper) 74LS138 3 to 8 line decoder in place of the 74LS154 4 to 16 line type. Figure 35 shows connection details for a 74LS138 used in this way.

An alternative way of doing things is to use outputs 8 and 9 of IC4 to control a CMOS flip/flop formed from a couple of gates from a 4001BE quad 2 input NOR gate, as shown in Figure 36. One of the spare gates acts as an output buffer stage, but the other

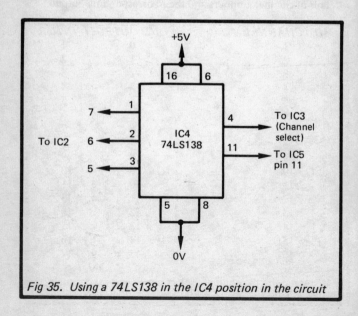

Fig 35. Using a 74LS138 in the IC4 position in the circuit

gate is left unused. The flip/flop is a simple set/reset type which, due to the inclusion of steering diodes D1 and D2, responds only to negative input pulses. When a note-on code is received, output 9 of IC4 pulses low and sets the output of the flip/flop high. When a note-off code is received output 9 of IC4 pulses low and resets the output of the flip/flop low again. This method of doing things is theoretically correct, but is not a method that I would recommend despite this. The unit will obviously fail to work properly with a synthesiser which uses 1001 as both the note-on and note-off header code. By simply not decoding bit 4 at all, as suggested earlier, the circuit should work with equipment that uses the 1001 and 1000 codes and equipment that only uses the 1001 code number. In fact results seem to be perfectly acceptable if only the most significant bit is decoded. This would result in a malfunction if header codes other than the note-on and note-off values were received, but in practice there would be no need for other header codes to be sent to whatever channel was assigned to the interface.

For some applications a gate pulse generator is all that is required, and an example this would be where a monophonic

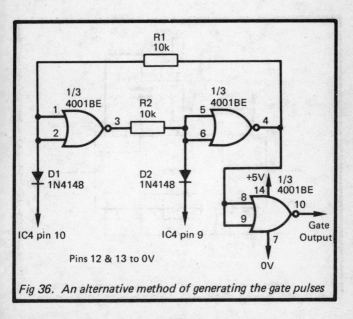

Fig 36. *An alternative method of generating the gate pulses*

synthesiser is being used as a percussion generator. With many percussive sounds the CV from the keyboard or CV input is irrelevant, and all that is needed is a pulse to trigger the sound. Another example would be where a percussion synthesiser of some kind is being controlled by the unit. These mostly only require trigger pulses, with the pitch (where appropriate) being preset via panel controls. A range of percussion synthesisers for use with the converter will not be described here, but some inexpensive and useful designs can be found in "More Advanced Electronic Music Projects" (Book No. BP174), from the same publisher and author as this publication.

One problem that might be encountered is that of the gate pulse being of an unsuitable duration. It is unlikely that the pulse would ever be too short, but it could sometimes be excessively long. This could occur where a percussion synthesiser requires a very short trigger pulse, but the gate pulse is originating from a keyboard which is providing a pulse length of perhaps one hundred milliseconds or more. This problem is easily overcome by using the circuit of Figure 37. A CMOS 4047BE monostable/astable device is connected here in the positive triggered monstable

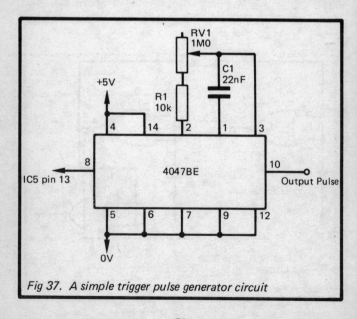

Fig 37. A simple trigger pulse generator circuit

78

mode. It therefore provides an output pulse at the commencement of each gate pulse, and the pulse duration is determined by the values of timing components C1, R1, and RV1. RV1 enables the pulse duration to be adjusted from about 1ms at minimum value up to about 100ms at maximum value, which should cover most (probably all) requirements. The monostable is a non-retriggerable type, and the circuit can therefore act as a pulse shortener or a pulse lengthener. Provided the input pulse is long enough to trigger the circuit (which in this application it must always be), the output pulse duration is totally independent of the input pulse width.

Another problem is that of devices which require a gate signal other than a positive pulse at standard 5 volt logic levels. Most instruments still in fact operate perfectly well with this type of signal, but there are a few that will not. Some of these can be quite difficult to interface to standard logic levels, but one type that is not is the so called "short to ground" gate input. These simply require a short circuit across the input during the gate pulse. The necessary gate pulse to short circuit conversion can be provided using a VMOS transistor connected as shown in Figure 38. Although a VN10KM is suggested for the VMOS device, practically any type will suffice (VN46AF, VN66AF, VN67AF, etc.).

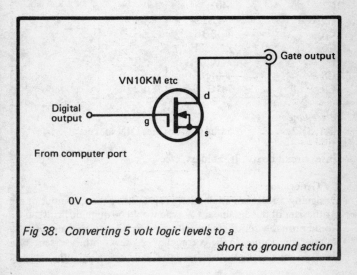

Fig 38. *Converting 5 volt logic levels to a*
short to ground action

MIDI To CV Converter Components (Figs. 33, 39 and 40)
Resistors all ¼ watt 5%

R1	270R
R2, R5	390R
R3	47k
R4	10k
R6	10k
R7	3k9

Potentiometers

RV1	10k preset
RV2	22k preset
RV3	10k linear

Capacitors

C1	10μF 25V electrolytic
C2	100nF polyester
C3	100μF 10V electrolytic
C4	1μF 50V electrolytic
C5	10nF polyester

Semiconductors

IC1	CNY17 or similar
IC2	6402
IC3, IC4	74LS154
IC5	4013BE
IC6	ZN428E
IC7	741C
IC8	4001BE
IC9	741C

Miscellaneous

SK1, SK2	5 way (180 degree) DIN socket

Case, circuit board, IC holders, etc.

CV Generation
Designing a MIDI to analogue circuit to drive the CV input of a synthesiser of the old linear CV type would be quite difficult, and would probably require a logarithmic amplifier to give an output voltage conforming to the correct law. As few synthesisers are of this type anyway it is not a subject that will be persued futher here.

Driving a logarithmic CV input is a much more straightforward task. The standard law is 1 volt per octave, but for the present application this is more usefully viewed as 83.33mV per semitone (1 volt divided by twelve semitones=0.08333 volts, or 83.33mV). In other words, we require a digital to analogue converter circuit that provides an output which increments in 83.33mV steps, so that it converts the values from the UART into corresponding voltages to drive the CV input of the synthesiser. This is very simple as an ordinary linear digital to analogue converter provides an output which increments in steps of equal amplitude, and it is just a matter of getting the scaling right. This can be accomplished using a variable gain DC amplifier at the output of the digital to analogue converter. The only other problems are to make sure that the circuit only responds to the correct bytes of information from the UART (the second byte in each group), and that the data is latched into the digital to analogue converter.

The circuit of Figure 39 is for a suitable digital to analogue converter circuit. This operates in conjunction with the MIDI to gate pulse converter circuit (Figure 33) and is of no value in isolation. The circuit is based on a ZN428E digital to analogue converter (IC6) which is ideal for the present application as it has a built-in 8 bit data latch. It would not actually be too difficult to design a circuit using a digital to analogue converter which lacks this facility, together with an external 8 bit data latch. However, from the constructional point of view things are greatly simplified by the use of a device which has the latch built-in.

The converter is a standard R-2R type, and as such it consists basically of a complex resistor network, eight electronic switches, and a precision reference voltage source. In this case the latter is a 2.55 volt type, and it has C4 and R5 as its discrete decoupling capacitor and load resistor respectively. A detailed theoretical discussion of this type of converter would be out of place here, but the general scheme of things is to have the precision voltage source feeding into the resistor network. The output is tapped off from the resistor network via the electronic switches, which are controlled by the 8 bit input signal. The resistor network is designed to provide an output voltage that is appropriate to the binary input value. The full scale output voltage is equal to the potential provided by the precision reference source.

In this case the full scale output potential is obviously 2.55 volts, and with input values in the range 0 to 255 (decimal) this gives increments of 10 millivolts. This is not actually the case in the

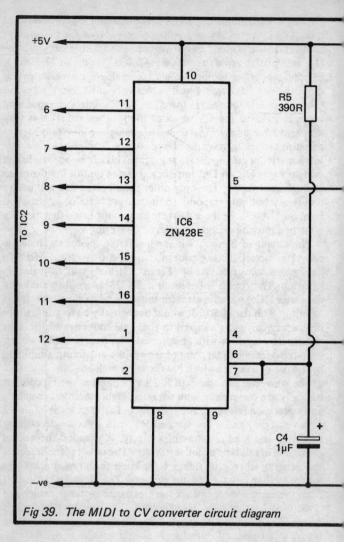

Fig 39. The MIDI to CV converter circuit diagram

present application since the UART is only providing a 7 bit output, with the most significant bit always set to 0 for note values. Accordingly, the most significant bit of the UART is left unconnected, and the other seven bits are connected to the seven

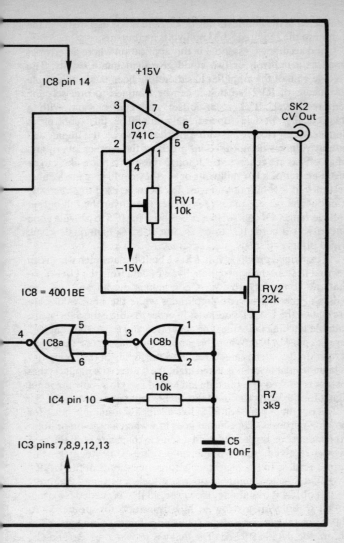

most significant inputs of IC6. The least significant input of IC6 is simply tied to earth. This halves the resolution of IC6 and boosts the output to increments of 20 millivolts. This is still less than the present application demands, but IC7 is an operational amplifier connected in the non-inverting mode, and this is used to boost the output to the required 83.33 millivolts increments.

Good accuracy is essential in this application where an error as small as a millivolt or two could give inadequate results. The voltage gain of the amplifier has therefore been made adjustable (by means of RV2) so that it can be trimmed to precisely the required level. RV1 is an offset null control, and with a theoretically perfect operational amplifier this control is unnecessary. However, with practical devices the input and output voltages do not take up precisely the correct levels, and small offsets are generated. Although these offsets are likely to be just a matter of a few millivolts or so, they could give inadequate accuracy at low output voltages. RV1 can be used to effectively trim out the offsets and give good accuracy over the full output voltage range. Of course, it is as essential for IC6 to provide good linearity as it is for IC7 to do so, but IC6 is a high quality type which offers extremely good accuracy.

As explained previously, IC6 has a built-in data latch which can be used to store the appropriate bytes of data from the UART, so that the converter provides a continuous output and not just pulses at the appropriate amplitudes while the note values are present on the UART's outputs. In order to utilize the data latch a suitable latching pulse must be generated and fed to the "enable" input at pin 4 of IC6. When this input is low, the data on the inputs is fed into the latches and through to the inputs of the converter. When the enable input is taken high, the data on the inputs at that instant is latched into the data latch, and used to supply the input signal for the converter until the enable input goes low again.

The output at pin 10 of IC4 almost supplies a suitable pulse for latching purposes. This output goes low when a note-on or note-off header code is received, and it stays in that state until the next byte is received, which is the note value. Unfortunately, this output returns to the high state before the outputs of the UART have had time to stabilise at their new logic levels, and the direct output of IC4 is unsuitable. However, all that is needed is a delay circuit to hold off the low to high transition for around 50 to $100\mu s$, so that the outputs are allowed sufficient time to stabilise before the data is latched. The delay is provided by R6 and C5, with two gates of IC8 connected as a non-inverting buffer to provide sufficient drive and a suitably shaped pulse to drive IC6 properly.

There is a slight flaw in this system in that during the period when the header code is present, this value will be fed through to the inputs of the converter. In practice this should not have any detrimental effect on the operation of the circuit as the period during which this occurs will be very short indeed. Depending on the source of the signals, it will only be from around $330\mu s$ to a few milliseconds at most.

Adjustment

If possible it is best to start with the unit disconnected from the analogue synthesiser and to use a multimeter set to a low DC voltage range (about 10 volts full scale) to monitor the CV output potential. The negative test lead goes to the 0 volt rail and the positive test lead connects to IC7 pin 6. Start with RV1 and RV2 both adjusted to a roughly mid setting. In order to adjust RV1 and RV2 correctly it is necessary to send suitable values to the interface. These can be obtained from either a MIDI equipped instrument or computer plus a MIDI interface. The computer offers the better option as it enables any desired values to be sent to the interface, whereas most MIDI equipped instruments operate over something less than the full 127 note range. When using a computer as the source bear in mind that it is no good just sending a series of test values to the interface. In order to latch data into the interface the note values must be preceded by the note-on code plus the appropriate channel value.

Start by using a fairly high note value, and one which is exactly divisible by 12. We will assume that 72 is selected, which is exactly six octaves up from the base note, and therefore represents an output potential of 6 volts. RV2 is accordingly adjusted for an output potential of exactly 6 volts. Next choose a low value, and again it is easier if the value is exactly divisible by 12. In fact 12 is a good choice of value, and one which corresponds to an output potential of 1 volt. RV1 is then adjusted to trim the output voltage to precisely 1 volt. This procedure is repeated a few times until the unit tracks accurately between the two values, and no further improvement in accuracy can be obtained.

The CV output of the converter can now be coupled to the CV input of the synthesiser using a standard jack lead. The gate output can be coupled to the synthesiser's gate input, but if the synthesiser has some facility which enables notes to be held on continuously (such as a "drone" switch), then it is probably better to use this. Note that many synthesisers will not respond to signals on the CV and gate inputs unless they are set up to do so. The control settings required to do this vary from one instrument to another, and if in any doubt the instrument's manual should give details of the correct settings.

It is unlikely that the initial adjustments will have set up the converter with sufficient accuracy to give good results over the full note range. On the other hand, any pitch errors should be quite small. The final adjustment consists of adjusting RV2 so that good pitch accuracy is obtained at the high note end of the range, and adjusting RV1 for good pitch accuracy at the low end of the range. This is a matter of tuning the synthesiser by ear against a tuning-fork, pitch- pipes, or an instrument which is accurately in-tune. Alternatively, by switching between the CV input and the keyboard the converter can simply be adjusted to give the same notes as those provided by the keyboard.

If a multimeter is not used to initially bring the converter close to correct alignment, the setting up procedure is in other respects the same. However, it will probably take longer to get to the stage where the unit is close to the correct settings if all the adjustments are made using pitch comparisons, even if you have a good sense of pitch. Where possible the initial adjustment with the aid of a multimeter is therefore strongly recommended. Incidentally, the converter will cover the full 127 note range of the MIDI system, which represents an output voltage range of 83.33 millivolts to a little over 10 volts. Some analogue synthesisers will operate over this full range, but not all will work properly with CV inputs as high as 10 volts. On the other hand, most analogue synthesisers have a keyboard range of only about two or three octaves, but this is not generally indicative of the maximum available range, and most instruments provide a much wider pitch range via the CV input. The manual for each instrument should give details of the acceptable CV input voltage range, but if in any doubt a little experimentation should soon reveal the usable range.

It has been assumed here that potentials of 1 volt, 2 volts, 3 volts, etc., correspond to the note "C". It has also been assumed that an output potential of 5 volts gives middle C from the synthesiser. With all the synthesisers I have ever encountered an input potential of 1 volt has always corresponded to "C", but if it does not with your particular synthesiser this will probably not matter. Most instruments have the ability to offset the tuning by up to an octave, and adjustment of the appropriate control will enable the sythesiser to be brought into agreement with the MIDI instrument(s). This facility is a useful one even if your synthesiser is correctly aligned with the MIDI instruments when this control is at its normal setting. You may wish to have the analogue synthesiser playing (say) a fifth higher than the MIDI instrument with which it is paired, and adjustment of the "tuning" or "frequency" control should permit this.

The problem of the analogue instrument playing the wrong octave is one that might be more difficult to solve. Most analogue synthesisers have an octave switch which can be used to shift the compass up or down an octave, or in some cases maybe even up or down two octaves. With some instruments, even with the octave switch at its lowest setting, it might be found that a MIDI note value of 60 gives an output pitch one or two octaves higher than middle C. Even if this should occur, the system is still obviously quite usable, if somewhat less than ideal, but it could obviously be better if the output voltage of the converter could be shifted downwards by one or two volts. This could shift the compass of the synthesiser down by an octave or two, bringing it into agreement with the MIDI instruments. A shift facility of this type is quite useful anyway, as it enables the synthesiser to be purposely tuned to the wrong octave if desired, and obviously adds to the shift range provided by the synthesiser itself.

It is not difficult to provide shift control for the unit, and basically all that is required is a variable voltage source. The lower end of R7 (which previously connected to the 0 volt supply rail) then connects to this voltage source. Raising the lower end of R7 above ground potential has the effect of reducing the output potential of IC7. The output potential is reduced by a fixed amount, and if the output voltage is reduced from (say) 3 volts to 2 volts, where the output would normally have been 4 volts it will be 3 volts, where it would have been 5 volts it will be 4 volts, and so on. This is, of course, precisely the action we require.

It is important that the voltage source should be highly stable or it will lead to drift and necessitate frequent readjustment of the alignment controls. The digital to analogue converter chip (IC6) contains a highly stable 2.55 volt reference source, and this is the obvious choice as the offset voltage source. All that is needed to give a variable reference voltage is a potentiometer and an operational amplifier to provide buffering, as shown in the circuit diagram of Figure 40. With the slider of RV3 at the bottom of its track the converter should function normally, and can be set up in the manner described previously. Moving the wiper of RV3 up the

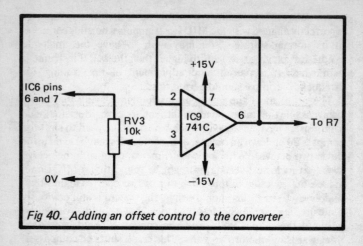

Fig 40. Adding an offset control to the converter

track introduces a steadily increasing offset voltage, and it is just a matter of adjusting RV3 for the required drop in voltage and pitch. Adjustment of RV3 might necessitate some slight readjustment to RV1 and RV2 in order to maintain perfect alignment, but any readjustment that is required should be absolutely minimal. With RV3 included in the circuit it would probably be better to use ordinary panel mounted potentiometers for RV1 and RV2 instead of preset types.

Power Supply

The converter has rather awkward power supply requirements in that three supply rails (plus the 0 volt rail) are required. The requirements are +5 volts, +15 volts, and −15 volts. Only a few milliamps is drawn from the +15 volt and −15 volt supplies which only power the operational amplifier (IC7), plus operational amplifier IC9 as well if the offset control is fitted. The 5 volt supply has a somewhat higher current drain at around 100 milliamps or so.

Batteries are not a very practical form of power source for a circuit having these power requirements, and a mains power supply unit is the only practical solution. The circuit diagram of a suitable mains power supply unit appears in Figure 41. This is a totally conventional circuit which uses rectifiers D1 and D2 to generate the basic negative supply with C11 providing smoothing.

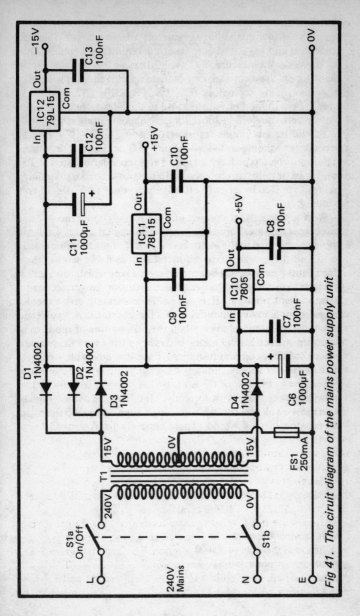

Fig 41. The ciruit diagram of the mains power supply unit

89

D3, D4, and C6 provide the same function but for the positive supplies. Monolithic voltage regulators are used to provide well smoothed and regulated outputs at the required potentials. Due to the low output currents involved, none of the regulators dissipate much power and none of them should require a heatsink. The decoupling capacitors (C7, C8, C9, C10, C12, and C13) should be mounted physically close to their respective regulator chips where they will be most effective at combatting instability.

T1 can be any mains transformer having a 15 – 0 – 15 volt secondary winding rated at about 200 milliamps or more. Alternatively, a type having twin 15 volt secondaries rated at 200 milliamps or more can be used, with the two secondary windings being connected in series to effectively produce a 15 – 0 – 15 volt winding.

With a project that connects to the mains supply the normal safety precautions should be observed. If a metal case is used this should be earthed to the mains earth lead. If a non-metallic case is used, but there is any exposed metal such as fixing screws, then these must be earthed. The case must be a type which has a screw fixing lid or cover so that easy access to the dangerous mains wiring is not possible. It is advisable to insulate any exposed connections at mains potential so that there is no risk of an electric shock being sustained even when the lid or cover of the case is removed. Check all the mains and other wiring very thoroughly before switching on and testing the unit. It is advisable to check that the power supply circuit is functioning properly before it is connected to the rest of the unit. Be very careful to connect the outputs to the main circuit correctly. Muddling one of the supplies with the +5 volt one could result in expensive damage to the main circuit (the UART would almost certainly be destroyed for a start).

Power Supply Components (Fig. 41)
Capacitors

C6,11	1000μF 25V electrolytic
C7,8,9,10,12,13	100nF ceramic

Semiconductors

D1 to D4	1N4002
IC10	7805
IC11	78L15
IC12	79L15

90

Miscellaneous

T1	Standard mains primary, 15–0–15 volt secondary rated at 200mA or more
S1	Rotary mains switch
FS1	20mm 250mA quick-blow

Case, circuit board, 20mm fuseholder, etc.

Extra Channels

If a multichannel converter is required, one way of achieving this would be to build a separate converter for each channel. Some saving in the component count could probably be achieved by having IC1, IC2, IC3, and their associated components common to all channels. A different output of IC3 would be used to drive each IC4, and the latter would need to be duplicated for each channel, as would IC6, IC7, etc. One problem that this would lead to is that of excessive loading on the UART's outputs, but an 8 bit TTL buffer should solve this problem. This is all only put forward as a suggestion for suitably experienced readers who would like to experiment with a multichannel system, and the prototype has only been tried and tested in single channel form. However, in theory there should be no difficulty in producing a multichannel unit.

MIDI Expander

With a complex MIDI set up there can be problems in finding sufficient outputs for every input you wish to drive. Many items of MIDI equipment have a "THRU" socket which enables the chain method of connection to be adopted without difficulty, but not all MIDI equipment is suitably equipped. The easiest solution to the problem is to have a simple splitter circuit along the lines of the circuit shown in Figure 42. A signal fed into one socket is available from the other two, but as this is a purely passive circuit there is a limit to the amount of expansion that can be provided. Most MIDI outputs seem to be able to drive two MIDI inputs without any difficulties arising, but driving more inputs than this would probably not be possible.

Where more than two outputs are required the circuit of Figure 43 can be used. This has an opto-isolator at the input followed by common emitter switches which drive the output sockets. Only three output stages and sockets are shown in Figure 43, but it should be possible to add many more than this if required as the

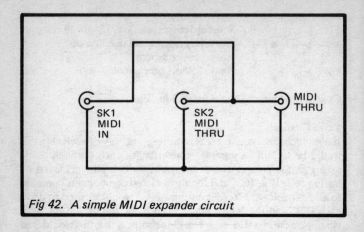

Fig 42. A simple MIDI expander circuit

opto-isolator provides plenty of drive. Being an active circuit it requires a power source, but this need be nothing more complex than four HP7 size cells connected in series. Suitable battery holders are readily available, and connections to these are via ordinary PP3 style battery clips.

MIDI Expander Components (Fig. 43)
Resistors all ¼ watt 5%
R1, R5, R8, R11	270R
R2	1k
R3, R6, R9	4k7
R4, R7, R10	1k8

Semiconductors
| IC1 | CNY17 or similar |
| Tr1, Tr2, Tr3 | BC549 |

Miscellaneous
| SK1 to SK4 | 5 way DIN sockets |

Circuit board, case, power source, etc.

In Conclusion
Hopefully the projects and information in this book will prove helpful to anyone setting up a MIDI system, or trying to add MIDI

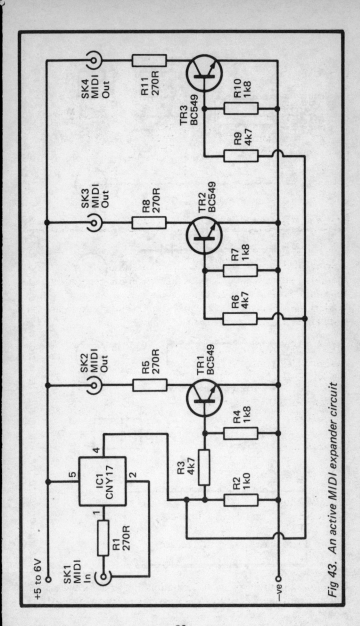

Fig 43. An active MIDI expander circuit

93

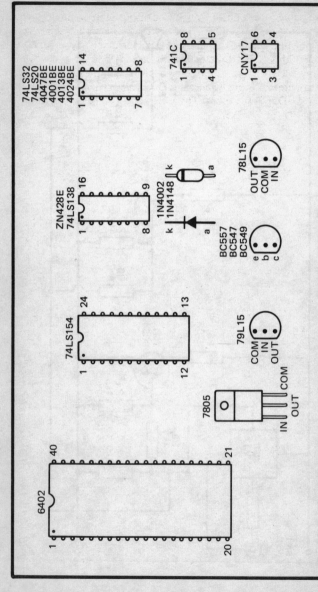

Fig 44. Semiconductor pinout details (transistor base views, IC top views)

94

equipment into an existing analogue set up. MIDI offers tremendous possibilities even when using quite a modest and inexpensive system, and it is well worthwhile spending some time studying the manuals for any MIDI instruments you have to discover the full MIDI capabilities of each one. It is also well worthwhile spending a lot of time experimenting with various set ups to determine just what can be achieved when using various bits of MIDI gear together. There are almost endless possibilities.

ALSO OF INTEREST

ELECTRONIC MUSIC PROJECTS   **BP74**
R.A. Penfold

Provides the constructor with a number of practical circuits for the less complex items of electronic music equipment, including such things as fuzz box, waa-waa pedal, sustain unit, reverberation and phaser units, tremelo generator, etc.

The text is divided into four chapters as follows: Chapter 1, Guitar Effects Units; Chapter 2, General Effects Units; Chapter 3, Sound Generator Projects; Chapter 4, Accessories.

0 900162 94 5   *112 pages*   *1980*   **£2.95**

MORE ADVANCED ELECTRONIC   **BP174**
MUSIC PROJECTS — **R.A. Penfold**

Intended to complement the first book (BP74) by carrying on where it left off and providing a range of slightly more advanced and complex projects. Included are popular effects units such as flanger, phaser, mini-chorus and ring-modulator units. Some useful percussion synthesisers are also described and together these provide a comprehensive range of effects including drum, cymbal and gong-type sounds.

0 85934 148 8   *128 pages*   *1986*   **£2.95**

MORE ADVANCED MIDI PROJECTS   **BP247**
R.A. Penfold

The projects in this book fall into two main categories: those that are designed to overcome a deficiency in an item of equipment in the system and those that are designed to enhance the performance of the system or to make it easier to use. Included are circuits for a MIDI indicator, THRU box, merge unit, code generator, pedal, programmer, channeliser and analyser.

These projects are generally more complex than those featured in book number **BP182 'MIDI Projects'**, although a few simple units have been included as well. While most of the projects are not suitable for beginners, they should be well within the capabilities of someone who has a reasonable amount of experience in electronics construction.

The circuits should also provide some useful electronic building blocks for use in readers' own designs.

0 85934 192 5   *128 pages*   *1989*   **£2.95**

Notes

Notes

Notes

Notes

Notes

Please note following is a list of other titles that are available in our range of Radio, Electronics and Computer Books.

These should be available from all good Booksellers, Radio Component Dealers and Mail Order Companies.

However, should you experience difficulty in obtaining any title in your area, then please write directly to the publisher enclosing payment to cover the cost of the book plus adequate postage.

If you would like a complete catalogue of our entire range of Radio, Electronics and Computer Books then please send a Stamped Addressed Envelope to:

BERNARD BABANI (publishing) LTD
THE GRAMPIANS
SHEPHERDS BUSH ROAD
LONDON W6 7NF
ENGLAND